HAUNTED
LIVERPOOL 12

To Julia Hoffman

© Tom Slemen 2006

Published by The Bluecoat Press, Liverpool
Book design by March Graphic Design Studio, Liverpool
Printed by Universities Press, Belfast

ISBN 1 904438 39 3

Tom Slemen

HAUNTED
LIVERPOOL 12

The Bluecoat Press

CONTENTS

CAPTAIN BLOTTO

So many long-forgotten characters went largely unnoticed by the chroniclers of nineteenth century Liverpool, who, in their annals, seemed more concerned with aldermen, mayors and visiting monarchs, or with the recording of spectacular shipwrecks and warehouse fires, than with the lives and times of the idiosyncratic and exciting personalities who really formed the history of this great city.

In some of our once well-kept cemeteries it is sad to see how time and the weather have often obliterated the inscribed names of the long departed who were lucky enough to have their passing marked by a headstone or a sepulchre, but what of the countless souls of equal, or even greater importance, who now rest in unmarked pauper's graves?

Somewhere in Liverpool, the mortal unremembered remains of Captain Joseph Doyle lie in the worm-riddled clay; his final port of call. At Doyle's funeral service, his lifelong friend Mickey pleaded before the indignant priest to have the Captain committed to the deep – an equally anonymous end to the one he was destined for – but one that would be fitting for his friend, and, more importantly, which was in accordance with his wishes. However, the man of the cloth ignored Mickey's pleas and instead had the ragged old interrupter thrown out of the church. The roughly-hewn wooden coffin was subsequently carted away without ceremony to be buried twelve feet down in a communal grave with forty-five others.

Let us not dwell on the sad fate of Captain Blotto, but instead, let us go back many decades, to a happier time and place, where Mickey and the Captain lived on little more than their wits and the tangy salt air in the Liverpool of days gone by. Let us go, by way of our imagination, back to one of the famous drinking holes of the city which the pair used to frequent, to one rainy Saturday afternoon in the tail-end of the summer of 1885.

Captain Blotto was almost legless in the Legs of Man public house at Number 1 Lime Street when his 'agent' and long-suffering friend Mickey York burst into the pub with a piece of astounding good news. So excited was Mickey that he addressed the drunken mariner by his actual name, which Captain Blotto hadn't heard spoken in years, and so he didn't answer to it at first.

So far gone was the Captain that Mickey had to tap him on the shoulder to elicit any kind of a response.

"Mickey, me old mate!" cried Captain Blotto, his bloodshot eyes widening. "Someone told me you had died."

His words were slurred and he swayed on his chair and cackled inanely, then pinched his little friend's cheek.

"Get off, Blotto!" said Mickey, slapping his hand away and guiding the Captain to a quiet corner of the pub where he could explain in private the job he'd landed for them. In whispered tones he explained that four men had approached him wanting a passage to Dundrum Bay in Ireland – that night. It was all very hush-hush.

Captain Blotto recoiled and shook his jowls in dissension, grabbing on to the arms of his chair to stop himself from toppling off it; he couldn't possibly sober up in time to undertake such an early sailing. However, all it took to bring him to his senses was the mention of a large amount of money and the word 'gold' and within the hour the duo were down at the docks, onboard the *Nelly Boyle*, ready for the passage to Ireland.

The four passengers looked highly suspicious, sneaking on board, cloak and dagger style, and the Captain immediately took them to be criminals on the run from the law. It has to be said that they were equally unimpressed with him, and the leader of the felons openly sniggered at his intoxicated state and shabby appearance. He then began to question his abilities as a mariner, saying he did not look fit to be a ship's captain. Captain Blotto appeared to be deeply affronted at this slight and countered it by haughtily declaring that he came from "a long seafaring dynasty". Even Mickey smirked at this preposterous claim. He had often heard the far-fetched tales about Blotto's father being a well-to-do mariner who had commanded the first ships to set sail for America – pure wishful thinking in his opinion.

The rain had cleared by evening, and so the *Nelly Boyle* sailed under a full moon through the waters of Liverpool Bay with the four crooks roped in to serve as a skeleton crew.

"Blotto! Watch those sandbanks!" cried Mickey in alarm and he visibly trembled as he gazed over the ship's rail into the foam-capped waves.

At the helm, with his minuscule pipe wedged between his teeth, the Captain squinted at the heavens.

"That there is the North Star," he said, pointing skywards, "and that will guide us straight to Dundrum Bay. Keep your eyes peeled for that star, me boys."

This very crude method of navigation failed to inspire any confidence in the ad hoc crew and they exchanged glances of disgust. What had they let themselves in for, they must have been stupid, putting their lives in the hands of this numbskull. Then, at two o'clock in the morning, one of the crooks raised the alarm when he noticed that Captain Blotto was now slumped over the wheel, snoring like a beached grampus whale.

"Gloriana! He's been at the rum again!" cried Mickey, sniffing the Captain's breath.

One of the crooks fetched a pail of water from the hold and hurled it at straight at Blotto's face.

"Abandon ship!" cried the semi-conscious inebriate, imagining the worst as the water crashed over him.

Enough was enough, and Mickey was not at all surprised when the criminals decided that they would rather keep their money and steer the ship to Ireland themselves, rather than trust an incompetent drunk at the wheel. Mickey and the Captain were marched to the stern at gunpoint by the mutineers.

"You're going in the drink, you drunken buffoon," hissed one of the blackguards, his pistol trained on Blotto's face.

Just then, a lone rogue albatross cried out above in the moonlit sky, a sure ill omen if there ever was one in the eyes of Captain Blotto.

"Oh, I don't like that at all," he said, shaking his head. "No! I don't like that one little bit."

"What are you gibbering on about now?" asked the villain, still with the loaded pistol just inches from Blotto's face.

"An albatross at night," croaked Blotto gravely, "means death will soon be upon us."

The pistol-packing felon's eyes narrowed with disbelief and he seemed ready to fire, when the sky above the *Nelly Boyle* suddenly began to burn with a faint red glow, and a ferocious wind whipped up from nowhere, rattling through the sails and blasting the Captain, Mickey and the crook with such tremendous force, that all three of them were knocked down on to the deck, like skittles in a bowling alley.

A ferocious bolt of lightning seared through the heavens and ripped through part of one of the topsails, and the ensuing thunder seemed to shake the very sea itself. Blotto had seem some tremendous storms at sea during his chequered career, but this one was worse than any of them. Could it be the Second Coming? he wondered to himself. Then he beheld a sight that was to haunt him for the remainder of his days. A pillar-shaped phosphorous glow started to bubble up out of the storm-rent skies. Seconds later, it materialised into a tall figure, dressed from top to toe in white, standing with its back to the three men on the deck before the wheel of the ship.

"A ghost!" muttered a terror-stricken Mickey, slowly picking himself up off the rain-lashed deck and backing away from the ghostly apparition.

Then, without warning, a wave of unprecedented size swept over the decks of the *Nelly Boyle*, sweeping three of the villains to their deaths in the raging sea. Mickey seized the opportunity to slam his fist into the gunman's face and the impact sent him tottering over the rail to join his partners in crime. A single muffled gunshot was heard below in the foaming saltwater hell, followed by a gurgling cry for help from a man whose lungs were obviously rapidly filling with seawater.

Captain Blotto trembled as he watched the quivering ghost slowly turn towards him and he was in for yet another shock that night, for the ghost was his father's, wearing his unmistakable sowester and long sealskin coat. Mickey was terrified, and he remained at the stern with his rosary frantically turning in his hand, but the Captain went over and spoke to the apparition, which had taken over the wheel and would steer the ship safely through the storm to Port Erin on the Isle of Man. Blotto could only watch in awe.

When they had reached the sanctuary of the port and lowered the anchor, the Captain attempted to hug his father, but found himself embracing nothing but empty air. His father's ghost had evaporated into the night sky, and as the crimson-tinted storm rolled back out into the Irish Sea, a solitary albatross flew with it towards the horizon. Could it be the same winged omen that had presaged this whole supernatural affair?

Back in Liverpool, later that same week, the frequenters of the waterfront taverns and city pubs couldn't help but notice a dramatic change in the character and demeanour of the notorious Captain Blotto. It was as if he had been reborn a sober man after the life-saving encounter with his beloved long-dead father. An old priest who had known Doyle and his family since he was a child, listened to the Captain's strange story after he had attended mass at St Anthony's Church the following Sunday.

"I don't expect you to believe me for one minute, Father. I know it sounds far-fetched, but I did see my father on the ship that night and he saved my life; and Mickey's life too," Doyle told the priest.

"Well, stranger things have happened, Captain," the smiling elderly priest said, "with fishes and loaves ..."

"Thank you, Father."

The Captain appreciated the wise words of the man of the cloth and he said goodbye to the priest and left the church with his head bowed to the sharp north wind.

THE CROWN STREET BOGEYMAN

On the night of Thursday, 4 April 1901, two sweethearts embraced by the light of the full moon on Myers Street in the Edge Hill area of Liverpool. A seventeen-year-old butcher's delivery boy named Tommy Sullivan of Tunnel Road, kissed sixteen-year-old dairy-maid Mary Jane Watkinson of Smithdown Lane, but their lovers' tryst was to be short-lived that night. Burly neighbourhood policeman PC Old's beat included Myers Street and when he came across the young couple kissing in public at 8.45 in the evening, he advised them to go home immediately; "Especially with all of the strange goings-on in the area of late," he added.

For the past few weeks, the people of Edge Hill had been barricading themselves indoors every night after dark, for fear of encountering the Crown Street 'Bogeyman'. Only yesterday a reporter from the *Liverpool Echo* had visited these streets to interview some of the victims who had been chased by the huge shadowy figure which was frequently seen to emerge from the nearby coal yards.

PC Old had initially dismissed the stories as the work of an old local tale-spinner named O'Brien, that was until three of his own colleagues vouched for the reality of the evil apparition. The policemen – William Miller, Johnny Cassidy and Tucker Haldane – all lived in Edge Vale, and all had witnessed the sight of lumps of coal mysteriously rising up from the coal yards and raining down on a cottage in Myers Street, where every window had been smashed to smithereens. The weird bombardment had not been fleeting but had continued for a good half hour. The three policemen, looked upon by the Edge Vale folk as the guardians of their neighbourhood, fled indoors when they heard the heavy footfalls of something invisible go thumping by.

A dog was found dead in the street on the following morning, stiff with rigor mortis. Its teeth were bared and its lifeless eyes were nearly bulging out of their sockets in terror. The dog's owner was mystified because it had been perfectly healthy the day before, so something or someone had obviously frightened the poor animal to death.

Mary Jane was not one to argue with a policeman, so she reluctantly set off to walk to her home upon that April night, sheepishly glancing back twice at

Tommy, who was also stealing glances at her over his shoulder. PC Old watched as the girl passed under the soft illumination of the lamp-post and on down the moonlit street. In quick succession a number of dense clouds suddenly got up and obscured the moon. The policeman somehow sensed that something eerie was at large, and he whistled nervously to himself as he proceeded on his beat. Then through the night air came the unmistakable sound of a woman screaming which sent Tommy and the policeman running towards the place where they had last seen Mary Jane.

The lawman and the butcher's boy arrived on the scene at Smithdown Lane within less than half a minute. They found the girl cowering in a doorway with her hands over her head, whilst an old man wearing a nightcap and a strange pair of oversized spectacles stood nearby swamped by a long black coat. In one hand he clutched the rusty old hoop from a barrel and in the other a crumpled ball of newspaper. The pair immediately recognised Harold Evans, a wealthy seventy-six-year-old eccentric known as the 'Hermit of Edge Hill'. He lived alone at Number 17 Edge Vale, where he hoarded all the rubbish that he collected during his nocturnal wanderings. PC Old shook his head and told him to get home at once. Evans scurried silently off into the darkness without uttering a sound.

The policeman and Tommy then escorted Mary Jane directly to her home, both guiltily feeling that they should have taken her there in the first place, thereby saving her a great deal of distress. The girl's parents invited Tommy and the constable into the house, where PC Old confided that he and many others in the local police force believed that the hermit was behind the coal-throwing antics of the so-called ghost.

"But old Mr Evans is such a frail little thing," protested Mrs Watkinson, treating the policeman to a steaming mug of cocoa. "I'm sure he wouldn't hurt a fly."

"Aye," agreed her husband, "and what's more, that thing, whatever it may be, is said to be well over six feet in height, so how does that fit in?"

"Yes, so I've heard," said the policeman, "but light can play some very funny tricks at night. I had an old lady come up to me only the other evening, convinced that a man was following her. When I went to investigate it turned out to be the silhouette of a pillar box!"

Just then Mary Jane started to tremble again, and she turned to her father and asked: "Papa, are there really such things as ghosts?"

"Of course not, my dear," Mr Watkinson reassured his daughter, squeezing her hand gently in his fist, "It's just somebody playing a joke, that's all, and Constable Old here will soon apprehend the villain, you mark my words."

"Whoever it is, it can't be poor old Mr Evans," persisted Mary Jane's mother, "I mean, how could a man of his age and size possibly throw great lumps of coal as far as Myers Street? He just wouldn't have the strength."

Mary Jane was unconvinced and her bottom lip began to quiver.

"It's just somebody playing some prank that's all, Mary Jane," said Tommy, fidgeting with his straw boater.

This was the first time he'd been in Mary Jane's home, and he felt terribly self-conscious under the critical gaze of her parents, particularly since he felt that he should have seen her safely home in the first place.

Each of them was going over their version of the events of the night when a succession of loud raps on the front door startled everybody, and Mary Jane let out a nervous yelp.

"Oh! My goodness! Who on earth can that be at this hour?" Mrs Watkinson asked in alarm.

PC Old sprang to his feet, put the mug of cocoa on the table and tapped his baton on his hand in a business-like manner as he went to the front door. He opened it to find an enormous caped colleague standing there in a downpour.

"Williams!" exclaimed PC Old. "Come on in out the rain, man. You look like a drowned rat."

PC Williams had just reached the bottom of Queensland Street on his beat, and at that point at 9pm each night, he normally encountered PC Old on the Smithdown Lane beat, and had gone looking for him when his friend didn't show up.

"How did you know I was here?" PC Old queried.

"The hermit told me," explained Williams, and described how he'd come across the strange old man wandering about near the coal yards, apparently in a daze.

Mrs Watkinson gave the soaked young policeman a mug of cocoa. This was turning out to be quite a party. He thanked her, gratefully sipping the delicious beverage. It was still tipping down with rain outside, so he decided that he would make this pleasant little interlude last as long as possible. He removed his helmet and dripping cloak, and sat down at the table next to Tommy Sullivan.

"Sir, have you seen the Bogeyman?" asked the lad.

"I haven't," replied PC Williams, "but I'm sure that that old hermit has got something to do with it."

"But what would he gain by all this nonsense?" Mr Watkinson asked, filling his pipe with tobacco.

"That, I cannot answer," said Williams, "but he's clearly not in his right mind walking the streets on a filthy night like this, picking up pieces of paper and rubbish and delving into people's dustbins."

"He's an old miser, so I've heard," added PC Old. He drank a mouthful of cocoa and continued, "And he owns shares in different companies and has a great deal of money in the bank, yet he still hoards all that rubbish in his rooms. A very peculiar old man and no doubt about it."

"But if he's a hoarder, why would he throw coal at people's houses?" Tommy asked, and went bright red when the two policemen both glared at him.

"You've got to admit the lad's got a point," Mr Watkinson smiled, puffing on his pipe and winking at his potential son-in-law.

As Williams and Old struggled to answer the butcher's boy, Mrs Watkinson posed another awkward question.

"Apart from anything else, how would a man in his seventies get into those coal yards? He'd have to climb over a twelve-foot high gate for a start. He couldn't possibly do it."

"Well, you can be sure that we'll catch whoever's responsible for all this nonsense, ma'am," PC Williams promised, trying to put a stop to the questioning which he felt was undermining his dignity as an officer of the law.

The nerve-straining antics of the Crown Street Bogeyman continued over the next few weeks, and even constables Williams and Old started to suspect that old Harold Evans might not be the culprit after all.

At the end of May, the neighbours of the seventy-six-year-old hermit became suspicious when they heard and saw no movement coming from within his home for well over a week, and so Emily Miller, the wife of a policemen who lived next door to Mr Evans, went into the house using a key he had given her. Emily had been the only person to befriend the old eccentric, and he had finally entrusted her with a key, with the proviso that it was only to be used for emergencies.

Emily shouted for her neighbour in the hallway, but received no reply. A vile, gut-wrenching odour hung thickly in the air, and Emily immediately suspected that it was the aroma of decomposition, so she called in her policeman husband William. Dreading what they might find, the couple slowly climbed the stairs, which were piled high with endless piles of rubbish. Holding handkerchiefs over their lower faces in an effort to keep the terrible stench at bay, they entered the hermit's bedroom. The room was buzzing black with bluebottles, which darkened every surface and blotted out most of the light from the windows.

William Miller rushed to the grimy cobwebbed windows and swept away handfuls of the loathsome flies. With great difficulty he managed to unfasten a rusty catch and let in a welcome rush of fresh air. He pushed up the window and turned to see the tragic, gruesome sight of the hermit's corpse, strewn halfway across the bed, with the feet just touching the floorboards, as if he had been attempting to leave his bed when he expired. Dozens of writhing maggots crawled across the bloated, fetid face, and clouds of great black flies crawled and swarmed all over him and under his nightshirt. Emily vomited at the sight, and her husband helped her downstairs and out into the fresh air, where a crowd of neighbours were eagerly waiting for news.

Harold Evans, the Hermit of Edge Hill, was dead. No Last Will and Testament could be found on the premises, and people immediately began to ponder on the fate of his rumoured fortune.

Even after his death, the gossip continued to spread about Harold Evans being behind the Bogeyman prank, but days later, on the very day of the hermit's funeral, a large chunk of coal bounced off the helmet of PC Old, and another piece hit him squarely in the back, winding him, as he walked past Martindale's coal yard on Smithdown Road. The policeman picked himself up off the floor, blew loudly on his whistle then whacked the kerbstone with his baton to signal for immediate assistance. Within minutes, three policemen were scaling the gates of the coal-yard. Twilight was falling, and they could see no one in the yard. Even after giving the yard a thorough search they could find nothing by way of a clue.

Days later, on the humid Sunday evening of 2 June, a full moon once again loomed in the sky over Liverpool, and its beams picked out Tommy and Mary Jane kissing in the alleyway off Myers Street. Tommy was whispering sweet nothings into his girlfriend's ears when he suddenly became quiet. He gasped and stepped back, looking up with an expression of disbelief, but Mary Jane thought he was just messing about, and giggling, said, "Stop trying to scare me, Tommy."

But she stopped in her tracks when she felt two enormous dark hands gripping her shoulders and then watched in horror as the long giant fingers slid down from her shoulders and on to her bosom. She tried to scream but her vocal chords were paralysed with fear and no sound came out. She fainted and slumped to the ground and the gargantuan hands released their vice-like grip. Tommy also found himself struck dumb as he gazed into the leathery purple wizened face of the weird-looking giant, which towered over him at a height the butcher's boy later estimated to be at least seven feet.

He scooped up the unconscious body of Mary Jane, then backed away with his legs buckling beneath him. He turned slowly, expecting the thing to seize him, but instead he heard deep unearthly laughter reverberating down the dark alleyway. His adrenaline finally kicked in and he started to run and he didn't stop, or look behind him, until he collapsed in a heap on the doorstep of Mary Jane's parents.

Mr Watkinson found the boy gibbering insensibly, still holding his unconscious daughter in his arms, and when he and Tommy carried the girl inside, she was revived by the fire amid the hysterical screams of her mother. When Tommy Sullivan told the Watkinsons what had taken place, they were doubtful at first. Was this lad really the right one for their daughter? He seemed to bring nothing but trouble. But when Mary Jane was able to talk, she backed up Tommy's story with her own account of the giant hands that had grabbed her in the alleyway.

The news of this latest attack by the Bogeyman sent shock waves rippling through the neighbourhood, made worse by later reports of a boy on Upper Parliament Street who had suffered a fit after waking in the early hours of the morning to find the silhouette of a large figure rapping at his bedroom window. The doctor who examined the boy opined that the fit had probably been brought on by a particularly lucid nightmare, which, in turn, had probably been fuelled, "by all the ridiculous hogwash about this so-called Bogeyman".

He was not the only one to hold such sceptical views of the recent goings on in Edge Vale.

"This whole affair is nothing but an epidemic of superstition among the ignorant classes," stated one Hugh Farrie, a pompous correspondent of a high-brow newspaper that was to feature the sensational circumstances relating to the 'Edge Hill Demon'.

A reporter from the *Liverpool Echo* investigated the strange haunting with a little more open-mindedness, and found that most of the Edge Vale inhabitants were too terrified even to comment on the thing which was disturbing the peace of their neighbourhood.

The weeks rolled by, and the sightings of the Crown Street Bogeyman became rarer, much to the relief of the locals and things eventually returned to normal. Just what the thing was that held a district of the city in a grip of fear will probably never be known now, but Heaven forbid, could the Bogeyman return one day?

Incidentally, the butcher boy Tommy Sullivan later married his sweetheart Mary Jane, and in their autumn years, whenever they sat around the fireside on a wintry night, they would often recall the uncanny tale of the weird creature that once prowled Edge Hill, to their many grandchildren.

ANAYA'S CURSE

In the 1740s, two brothers, John and James Hardman, both men of considerable wealth, lived at Allerton Hall, which today houses a pub in the grounds of Clarke Gardens. Both Hardmans were general merchants who had amassed their fortunes as ship-owners and slave dealers in the burgeoning port of Liverpool. John Hardman, a very forceful, no-nonsense type of man, had once been an MP for Liverpool, and was very proud and boastful about his long pedigree, and he harboured designs to have his twenty-year-old daughter Grace married off to a rich young man named James Perceval, a relative of the distinguished family who had once owned the Allerton Hall estate. Unfortunately, Grace felt nothing towards James, and tried her utmost to rebel against the arranged marriage.

One day, Grace mounted Quicksilver, her favourite horse, and rode out into the then unspoilt countryside of Allerton and Woolton, until she was forced by heavy rain to shelter under an oak tree overlooking a mansion built of dusky red brick faced with white stone. A coachman from the stately home approached her to inform her that she was trespassing on private land, but instead, the words died on his lips, because Grace was so beautiful, and obviously of such high birth, that she quite took his breath away. Instead of admonishing her, the coachman, John Hazlehurst, gallantly handed his coat to the shivering young heiress, and offered her his silver whiskey flask, from which she took delicate sips as they talked.

It was love at first sight on both their parts and they were so taken with each other's company that they didn't hear the galloping hooves of Sirius, John Hardman's Arabian horse, thundering towards them. The merchant drew the horse to a sudden halt before the couple, throwing up great clods of earth, and threatened to horsewhip Hazlehurst to death for accosting his daughter. Grace begged and pleaded for her father to have mercy upon the young coachman, explaining that he had only tried to help her. Still white with rage, Hardman lowered his whip with a snarl and ordered his daughter to mount her horse and to accompany him home at once.

Days later, one of John Hardman's ship's arrived in Liverpool, carrying a group of African slaves who had been delivered to the port to be 'trained' as domestic servants. Anaya, a young slave woman, obviously sick and painfully thin from the horrendous conditions of the voyage, stood shivering with fear, clutching her twelve-year-old daughter Dada. It was apparent to all those around that she was terrified that she and the child were going to be separated. The slave trade allowed no room for sentiment of any kind and the mother and daughter were cruelly wrenched apart upon Hardman's orders. Dada cried hysterically for her mother, and Anaya desperately tried to reach out for her child but she was roughly whisked away from the ship to Allerton Hall, where she would be trained to be Grace's personal maid.

As she was forcibly taken away, the broken-hearted mother pointed a thin black finger at John Hardman as he stood upon the deck of the ship, and roundly cursed him in her foreign tongue. Something about the woman was deeply menacing and Hardman asked the Captain what she was saying, and he translated it as: "White man, as my home is destroyed, so may your home be destroyed and taken from you; as my child has been taken from me, so may your child be taken from you and lost forever."

John Hardman laughed nervously at the woman's curse and tried to dismiss it to those around him as the rantings of an illiterate savage, but deep down he felt deeply troubled by this young mother's wrath.

Not long afterwards, under a midnight April full moon, and despite her father's strict orders to the contrary, Grace rendezvoused with the coachman John Hazlehurst in the stables of the hall, and they both decided to run away and get married. Grace mounted Quicksilver and John jumped on Sirius, and they galloped off into the night at breakneck towards the banks of the River Mersey. Two fishermen were bribed to take the couple across to the Cheshire side of the river, where they were soon married at Eastham village. The riderless horses found their way back to Allerton Hall and John Hardman quickly put two and two together and guessed what had happened. Quaking with rage, he summoned the family solicitor and within hours he had written his daughter out of his will. The solicitor helped him to draw up a new will, which not only disinherited his daughter, but also her husband and their immediate descendants for a period of ninety-nine years.

Anaya's curse had come to pass through his own doing; John Hardman had lost his child, and when he died the family lost his home, for despite the many Hardmans who claimed Allerton Hall to be rightfully theirs, none of them was successful, and in the end the estate passed automatically into the ownership of the City of Liverpool.

Incidentally, one claimant to the estate of Allerton Hall claimed to have legal documents to back up his claim, and he instructed a solicitor to go to the high court in London to press the case, but the solicitor was ambushed on his way to the capital. His broken body was found at the bottom of Allerton Delph – and all of the important documents pertaining to the case were missing from his ransacked leather briefcase, and were never to be found again.

John Hazelhurst and his wife Grace enjoyed a long and happy marriage and produced nine children.

GUARDIAN ANGELS

A guardian angel is said to be a spirit entity, or guide, who stays with a person throughout their life, protecting them from harm. A guardian angel can manifest itself in various forms, including a warning voice, a seemingly irrational hunch, or even as a 'forewarning dream'.

In 1964, a Walton woman named Maria, experienced a series of strange recurring dreams in which she actually died after being hit by a speeding car. Each time in the chilling dream, she was crossing a sunny street when she would suddenly become aware of a bald man walking alongside her. The dream would always end with Maria stepping out into the road and being hit by the car. She would land with tremendous force on her back in the road and then everything would fade to a suffocating blackness, through which would come a man's voice saying, "She's a goner."

The nightmares finally stopped persecuting her after a fortnight and her normal sleep pattern returned.

Then, one sunny day, Maria was walking through Liverpool city centre, towards St George's Crescent on Lime Street, when she noticed a bald-headed man walking alongside her. She instantly recognised him as the very same man who had appeared in her recurring nightmares. Maria and the man halted simultaneously at the curb, and he looked to his right, then left – facing Maria. There was no doubt about it, he was definitely the same man who had haunted her dreams, and Maria was so taken aback at the sight of the familiar-faced stranger, that she didn't step off the kerb as she had been about to do, but instead stood gazing at him in bewilderment. At that moment, a car driven by a reckless motorist came flying round the corner and careered past the two of them at breakneck speed, within inches of the kerb. Had Maria attempted to cross the road at that moment she would have had no chance of escape and would have undoubtedly been mown down by the dangerous driver.

As the car sped on by, the bald-headed man turned and walked away without uttering a sound and was soon lost in the milling crowds of Lime Street, but Maria was in for another shock when she turned the next corner. The car that had narrowly missed her had crashed headlong into a lamp-post, and a crowd of people were standing around the crumpled vehicle which was leaking petrol and had steam escaping from the broken radiator. One of the bystanders stepped forward and peered into the driver's window. After a few moments he drew away from the car and solemnly shook his head.

"The steering wheel's gone right into his chest," he announced, then bowed his head and added, "He's a goner."

Again, Maria had no difficulty in recognising the voice of the bystander as the same man who had said "She's a goner," in her disturbing dream.

Decades later, Maria was at home watching television when she suddenly saw the bald-headed man whose appearance on the Liverpool street in 1964 had saved her from being run over. There was no mistaking him, that face would be etched on her mind forever. It was Patrick Stewart, famous today for playing the role of Captain Jean-Luc Picard in *Star Trek: The Next Generation*. But what on earth would Stewart have been doing in Liverpool in 1964? Well, as it turned out, that year, Stewart was indeed in the city. He was working as a jobbing actor at the Liverpool Playhouse.

Maria has had other warning nightmares which have also saved her life, and she firmly believes that they are the work of her guardian angel.

~

A *Merseymart & Star* reader named Danielle recently related to me the details of a curious incident where her life was saved by a paranormal creature.

One morning in 1996, when Danielle was nineteen, at 1.30 in the morning, she left Reds nightclub on Edge Lane feeling slightly intoxicated. Very foolishly for a woman on her own, she decided to take a short-cut to her home on Salisbury Road by cutting through Wavertree Park, which was almost pitch black at that time in the morning.

Right in the middle of the park, Danielle was stumbling along in her ungainly platform shoes, when she suddenly caught sight of a figure emerging from the bushes in the nearby Botanic Gardens. She suddenly realised what a vulnerable position she had put herself in and she was so scared that she made the sign of the cross and started muttering her prayers. She had no alternative but to carry on, as there was no one else about who could help her. The whole park was deserted apart from the man who was heading in her direction from the bushes. She somehow felt that if she tried to break into a run the figure would immediately speed up and chase after her. So, trying to walk as fast as she could without actually running, she headed for the nearest set of gates, all the time aware that the sinister figure was closing in on her.

With a sinking heart she realised that she was not going to make it in time – the figure was almost upon her – when she realised that she was no longer alone. Apparently out of thin air, a huge white Alsatian dog had appeared, and it was walking closely alongside Danielle, as if to protect her. At one point the animal turned and growled menacingly, and a relieved Danielle saw the stalker run off back into the darkness. Walking as quickly as she could in her unsuitable footwear, she eventually reached the park gates and the relative safety of the well-lit streets. As soon as she dared, she looked back towards the blackness of the park. The dog sat there following her with its eyes – then literally vanished as the girl looked on.

To this day, Danielle believes that the dog was some kind of supernatural guardian sent to protect her in her hour of greatest need. Not surprisingly, she has never been tempted to test her theory a second time by using the shortcut across the park again.

Invisible Assailants

Throughout history there have been many reports of invisible assailants being on the loose. In 1876, for example, panic broke out on the streets of Nanking, China, when something invisible to human eyes started to snip off the pigtails which adorned the heads of nearly every Chinaman at that time. Many of the citizens were naturally sceptical about the 'Snipper' stories at first, until hundreds of people fell victim to the strange attacks.

In one incident, a hermit in Shanghai awoke in the middle of the night to find something pulling and tugging roughly at his hair. He jumped out of bed and lit a lamp only to find his neatly cut pigtail lying on the pillow. People walked about clutching their pigtails, living in dread of an encounter with the Snipper. The mystery deepened when an historian discovered that a similar, hair-cutting 'demon' had at been at large in China during the Wei dynasty, as long ago as AD 477.

Over the years I have amassed a bulging file documenting many local cases of such invisible assailants, and here are just a few accounts from that file.

In June 1957, a twenty-six-year-old office worker named Judith would often spend her lunch hour lying on the grass of Coronation Gardens, a pleasant green urban space which once existed off Paradise Street. A heat-wave was on at the time, and Judith would find the gardens crowded with other workers on their lunch breaks. One day she was looking for a good place to sit when a group of her workmates called her over to a sheltered corner of the gardens, and Judith sat down amongst them, kicked off her shoes, and reclined back, enjoying the tickling sensation of the warm grass on her bare feet. As she squinted up at the blazing sun in the clear blue sky, all thoughts of the dingy office in which she worked were blotted out for one blissful hour.

About a minute afterwards, as Judith was about to get up to go and buy an ice cream, she felt a sharp bite on her leg, and let out a squeal of pain. The distinct U-shaped impression of a row of human-like teeth was clearly visible on her calf – along with a faint smear of a saliva-like liquid. It was obvious that no one present had inflicted the bite-mark, and as Judith was examining her leg, her seventeen-year-old friend, a typist named Clair, also cried out in pain. In one swift movement, the girl jumped to her feet and inspected her forearm. Another bite impression, identical to the one on Judith's leg, had appeared on Clair's arm, and again there was a trace of saliva left by the unseen biter, which left her feeling disgusted.

The girls became so uneasy, that they reluctantly moved from the sunny gardens and went instead to a café.

At the time it was assumed that a ghost was behind the two biting incidents, but such speculation rarely throws any light on these types of phenomena. I personally believe that unknown species of beings live alongside us all the time, but in a different dimension, separated only by some wafer-thin partition between our world and theirs. Mischievous, curious, and perhaps simply evil, entities from this parallel world may occasionally breach the partition and intrude into our dimension to wreak all kinds of havoc.

One night in 1969, three drinkers left the Lord Clive pub on Belmont Road, when one of them, a man named Hugh, let out an agonised cry. Something or someone had slashed the left cheek of his face. As Hugh pressed a handkerchief to the smarting wound, something invisible to him and his two friends slashed his hand as well.

Curiously, on this occasion, the three men heard the soft padding sounds of someone walking away in the direction of Allen Street but could see no figure to correspond with the footsteps. Hugh's wounds were treated at the local hospital, and a doctor said he believed that a razor blade or Stanley knife had inflicted the cuts.

The eerie hair-cutting Snipper demon is apparently not confined to China. In 1971, a young Toxteth man named Jimmy Lowry left his local barber's on Lodge Lane with his hair newly coiffeured in the popular feather-cut style. In his black and white 'Budgie' jacket and new haircut, Jimmy cut a fashionable figure and was brimming with confidence as he made his way home, eyeing up all the girls he passed on the way.

However, on the following morning, the teenager awoke in his bedroom in Windsor Gardens and discovered great chunks of his hair missing. He was about to accuse his twelve-year-old sister when he learned that lengths of her own long hair had been hacked off during the night as well.

A week later, it was the turn of Jimmy's mother. Mrs Lowry went to bed in her curlers and hairnet, as usual, and when she awakened in the morning, she found whole strands of her own hair missing – along with her curlers and hairnet!

The family could come up with no feasible explanation for the nocturnal scalpings and for a long time afterwards went to bed in fear and trepidation that they would wake up the next morning to find even more of their hair lopped off in the night.

MUTCH WANTS MORE

Off London Road, in 1887, at Number 5 Falkland Street, there once lived a house painter and paper-hanger named John Mutch, who was suspected by the police of being a sophisticated career criminal, using his innocent daytime occupation as a front for his less savoury activities. Chief Superintendent George Williams of the Central Police Office at 111 Dale Street, was in no doubt that a calculating cracksman and cunning scoundrel lurked behind the respectable persona of the working-class decorator. Several police informers had repeatedly told Williams as much, but concrete proof was very hard to come by and he had to live with the frustrating knowledge that Mutch was laughing at himself and his force.

In March 1887, John Mutch, accompanied by his business partner Fred Tomkinson, and his diminutive twelve-year-old son Billy, were redecorating the elegant upper rooms of a mansion at Walton-on-the-Hill with exotic wallhangings which had been purchased at great expense by the master of the house, Sir Alexander Chalmers. Chalmers frequently came upstairs to supervise the progress of the decorators – he didn't want to risk having his investment ruined. On one occasion he bragged to the captive audience of workmen about his adventures in India, and then the topic of conversation turned to a recent series of burglaries that had been perpetrated in the area.

"Blighters even broke into Walton Vicarage. Nothing's sacred, what?" tutted Sir Alexander.

He then went to the corner of the room and lifted some heavy protective canvas sheets to reveal a large mahogany chest with a length and breadth of four feet, and a depth of five.

"The family silver," said Sir Alexander, touching the side of his nose as a sign of the shared confidence. "Can't take any chances with these blackguards about."

He then explained that he would shortly be off to visit relatives in Wales for two days, and during that time, the chest of silverware would be deposited in his bank for safekeeping.

"Imagine if anything happened to that. It's taken me years to get the collection together. From all around the world, you know. Irreplaceable."

Although his face revealed nothing, John Mutch treated the unasked for confidence as a gift from on high and less than an hour after Sir Alexander Chalmers had left the room, he had effortlessly opened the mighty chest with his picklock and was admiring the contents. He then leaned out of the window to confirm that his partner Fred Tomkinson was stationed, as planned, behind a hedge in the garden down below. Within minutes, great quantities of top quality silver plate, candelabra, and the rest of the family heirlooms had been dropped into Fred's expert hands and safely stowed in some waiting sacks. Mutch then drilled a number of small neat holes in the body of the chest and put back the heavy dustsheets just as he had found them.

At 3pm the butler, a footman and a coachman came to collect the chest. It was taken to the bank on Castle Street, and deposited there for the best part of two days whilst Sir Alexander was away. On the second day, a member of staff at the bank discovered that several boxes and chests in the strong-room had been rifled through and robbed, yet there was no sign of a forced entry into the vault, so the police concluded that it must have been an inside job, and paranoia took hold of the staff as suspicion fell from one employee to another.

Sir Alexander's chest was found to be still securely locked, and so it was transported back to the mansion at Walton-on-the-Hill by the same three servants. John Mutch and Fred Tomkinson watched with seeming lack of interest as the chest was placed in the same corner of the room by the three men. Shortly afterwards, the butler produced a large key and was about to open the chest and check on the contents, when Mutch suddenly pointed out of the window and yelled, "Someone's just climbed into the drawing room through the french windows!"

The butler was completely taken in by the ruse and dashed downstairs, alerting the other servants as he did so. Mutch quickly ran to the chest, and expertly used his skeleton key to open it, and out popped little Billy Tomkinson with a very cheeky smile on his face! He had got into the trunk before it was taken to the bank on Mutch's instructions and had lived on bread, biscuits and a flask of water in the chest for almost two days. In the wee small hours the fearless lad had emerged from the chest in the bank vault, and picked and smashed the locks of the other boxes in the strong-room, before putting the proceeds and himself back in the ventilated chest, and turning the key in the lock from the inside.

Like lightning, Mutch stashed the proceeds of Billy's handiwork into his spacious toolbag. He then took five house bricks from Fred's toolbag and put them in the chest and relocked it. When the butler later returned and unlocked the chest, he found nothing but the bricks and not a sign of the family silver. He scratched his head in disbelief.

"Anything wrong, mate?" asked Mutch.

"I just don't understand it," said the baffled butler. "All the silverware is missing and I will have to be the one to tell his Lordship."

"Cor, blimey! Can't even trust the banks these days," said Mutch, winking at little Billy behind the butler's back. What's the world coming to, that's what I'd like to know."

A furious Sir Alexander berated the bank for failing in its duty to protect his most precious possessions and was so appalled by the loss of his family's heirlooms that he withdrew his account that very day.

Mutch and his accomplices were involved in many other daring and ingenious robberies across Lancashire, Cheshire and Derbyshire, all the while maintaining his paper-hanging business as a cover.

SEEING DOUBLE

Statistically, somewhere in this world, each one of us must have an almost exact double, practically indistinguishable from ourselves. Whilst most people can accept this fact without too much trouble, it can still be extremely disconcerting if you should happen to meet your flesh and blood mirror image.

Imagine then what it would be like if people started seeing your twin – assuming you don't already have one – in your own city, or your local neighbourhood. It would cause some confusion to put it mildly, plus a little terror, if you encountered your own replica in the street.

Reports of ghostly doubles, or 'Doppelgangers' (a German word meaning 'double walker') to give them their official title, have been reported throughout history and throughout the world, and they are a fairly well-documented but poorly understood phenomenon. The following are just a few examples of how doppelgangers can manifest themselves in the lives of ordinary and not so ordinary people.

In 1603, Queen Elizabeth, the last Tudor monarch of England and Ireland, was startled, upon entering her bedchamber, to find the ghost of a woman stretched out on her bed. She was just about to summon the servants to oust the intruder, when she realised the shocking fact that the pale female was actually a mirror image of herself. Not long afterwards the Queen fell gravely ill, and despite leeching, blood lettings and the ministerings of the best physicians in the land, in March of that year she died 'from frailty and insomnia'. Many believed that the Queen had seen an omen of her own death that day, in the form of her pale and ghostly replica.

Seeing one's doppelganger is traditionally considered to be a sign of approaching death, but I have investigated many doppelganger cases, and this simply isn't the norm at all, although I have noted that a person's rogue double often goes walkabouts when the original is either seriously ill or under severe stress for some reason.

~

A case in point is the Carne Rasch incident of 1905. In May of that year, Sir Gilbert Parker, a Conservative MP, was attending a debate at the House of

Commons. This is what the MP had to say of something bizarre that took place in the Commons that day: "I wished to take part in the debate in progress, but missed being called. As I swung round to resume my seat I was attracted first by seeing Sir Carne Rasch out of his place, and then by the position he occupied. I knew that he had been very ill, and in a cheery way nodded towards him and said, 'Hope you are better'."

Sir Carne Rasch made no sign by way of acknowledgement and uttered no reply. This struck Sir Gilbert as rather odd to say the least, as the two men were usually on the best of terms. He then noticed that his friend's face was remarkably pallid, and his expression quite steely. In fact, it was an altogether stony expression; grim, almost resentful. Sir Gilbert continued: "I puzzled over his strange behaviour and demeanour for a moment. Then I turned again toward Sir Carne Rasch, but he had disappeared. That puzzled me, and I at once went in search of him. I expected, in fact, to overtake him in the lobby. But Rasch was not there. No one had seen him. I tried both the Whips and the doorkeeper, equally without avail. No one had seen Sir Carne Rasch."

At the time when Sir Gilbert had seen Sir Carne Rasch's double at the Commons, the original had actually been lying in bed, seriously ill, yet longing to attend the important debate at Parliament. Well, the rumour of Rasch's doppelganger spread like wildfire throughout Westminster and beyond, and he was widely expected to die, for according to the superstitious people who heard about the odd tale, such manifestations of one's 'wraith' were a forewarning of certain and imminent death.

Fortunately, however, Sir Carne Rasch eventually returned to good health, and when he appeared at the Commons, he was rather annoyed to find himself being poked by the fingers of curious colleagues who thought he might be a mere projection.

Besides Sir Gilbert Parker, two other people witnessed the pale phantasm of Carne Rasch that day. They were Sir Henry Campbell-Bannerman and Colonel Sir Arthur Hayter.

Locally, there have been numerous cases of doppelgangers being reported to me. Here are just a few of them.

~

After a spot of window shopping one overcast afternoon in April 1958, fifty-two-year-old Janet Morris walked around Lewis's Corner on Renshaw Street and hurried to the bus stop near the Newington public house. Her green corporation bus – which would take her to her home on Menlove Avenue – was just pulling up at the stop, and there was a crowd of people waiting to board the vehicle. However, as Janet dashed along towards the bus, her attention was suddenly caught by something very strange indeed; it was the back of a woman hurrying towards the bus in front of her. What was unusual was that she was wearing the exact same clothes as herself and even sported the same hairstyle. She too held a small envelope-style handbag, and then came the shock that halted Janet in her tracks. The lookalike turned around – and Janet could see that the woman also had her face. Her unearthly counterpart didn't seem to notice Janet as she glanced back. She looked straight through her, then mingled with the jostling crowd getting on to the bus.

Janet remained rooted to the spot in shock, wondering if she was going mad. The bus moved off along Renshaw Street, and Janet actually wondered if her counterpart had been some relation she did not know about, but she doubted it, because even if the woman had been an unknown relative, that still did not explain why she should be wearing the exact same clothes and even have the same hairstyle as herself.

Janet's husband, Frank Morris, listened to his wife's odd account of the flesh and blood replica, but all he had to say about it was: "Someone's probably playing some kind of trick on you."

"Why can't you believe me," asked his wife who was still feeling very shaky about the whole affair.

"I'm sorry, love. I can see you're upset, but I just don't believe in such things."

"But, Frank, she was as real as you or me."

Frank's scepticism was tested in the following week, when he himself saw the eerie clone of his wife as he was taking the dog for a walk along Menlove Gardens North. At first, he naturally assumed that the person he was looking at was his wife, even though he knew that she had gone to visit her mother in Whiston at that time. Perhaps she had returned early for some reason, Mr Morris thought, and he unleashed the dog so that he would run to her. The animal ran up to what seemed to be Janet from a distance, but upon reaching the figure, it came to an abrupt halt. A clump of hair on the canine's back reared up and he started to bark at the woman, then ran whining back to Frank, its tail between its legs.

"Jan!" shouted Mr Morris to his wife, but the figure walked on at a rather fast pace and Frank was unable to catch it up. He soon lost sight of the woman, and later discovered that his wife had still been at her mother's home in Whiston during the time he had set eyes on her mysterious double in Menlove Gardens.

The doppelganger was seen in many other places by various people, and Janet became so upset by the peculiar goings-on that she visited her doctor, and he admitted – rather reluctantly – that he too had seen her spooky mirror-image the week before. He had driven past her on Smithdown Place, where she was standing by a hairdresser's shop, and then a minute later the doctor had been baffled to spot the real Janet with her husband and daughter walking up Green Lane.

At the time of the doppelganger incidents, Janet was going through a difficult menopause, but once the hormonal turmoil had subsided, the mysterious twin was seen no more.

~

In yet another instance Joan of West Derby wrote to me to relate the story of her own mysterious clone.

Joan was sitting on a beach on Anglesey many years ago, when her husband decided to go and get them an ice cream each. Joan watched him go, and also surveyed her three children playing by the water's edge, when a rather familiar young lady appeared upon the scene. She was wearing the exact same type of summer dress as Joan, and she also had the very same face as the Liverpool woman. She came over to Joan and sat by her on the sand. Any casual observer would unquestionably have taken the two young women to be identical twins. For some reason Joan did not feel at all uneasy about seeing someone who was indistinguishable from herself.

Joan's husband returned and was stunned to be confronted by what looked like two identical wives. He wasn't even sure which one he should give the ice-cream cone to until the doppelganger of Joan stood up and wished her "Good luck" before walking away. The husband thought the alter ego of his wife was spooky but Joan felt quite at ease about the meeting, for reasons she couldn't quite articulate. She never saw that living mirror-image of herself again, but the unusual incident stuck in her mind for years.

THE BERMAC CASE

Paris in the 1890s will be forever characterised as the decadent era of the can-can and cabaret, but during this time, among the two million people living in the French capital, there operated a mysterious killer and swindler with a split-personality who went under many aliases.

In 1891 he called himself Roman Bermac, and in the autumn of that year, as a student named Marie Curie, who would save so many lives, was enrolling at the Sorbonne, Roman Bermac was busy killing people. He swindled a fortune from a Parisian businessman then hanged him and made it look like suicide. He even forged a suicide note, but the hanged man's wife questioned its validity, telling the police that she did not recognise the handwriting as that of her dead husband.

To cover his tracks, Bermac then dyed his hair red, shaved off his moustache, and took lodgings on the Boulevard of the Madeline, where he became a hermit for a while, drinking himself into a stupor with absinthe each night for over a month.

At around this time he attracted the attention of a poor young girl named Gauntlette, who had the unenviable job of cleaning his apartment. For some reason she felt some sympathy towards Bermac and treated him with respect. Unfortunately, in the mysterious depths of his split-personality mind, he imagined that she was an agent of the French Police, and before long had tried to strangle her, but she came to just in time and ran off to call the gendarmes. Bermac fled from the apartment carrying a case packed with the money that he had cheated his murder victim out of before his death.

He soon settled in another part of the capital, and took up his old drinking ways. One evening he discovered an envelope lying on a table in his apartment. Bermac opened the envelope and saw to his horror that upon a piece of paper in a childish scrawl, someone had written the words, 'I know what you did – murderer'. Bermac spun around and peered into all the dark corners of the apartment. Was somebody still hiding there, watching him? No, surely not. He noticed that the window was fastened from the inside, so decided that the culprit had to be the old landlord, for only he had access to the spare key to the apartment.

So, without further ado, Bermac invited the old man in for a drink, and then promptly strangled him to death without trying in any way to establish whether it really was he who had written the note.

Bermac then went to ground again in another arrondissement, this time settling for a draughty old garret left vacant by an artist who couldn't pay his rent. The only visitors to the garret were a boy named Guy who brought his meals, and the decrepit old landlady, Mona. Nevertheless, Bermac became totally paranoid and always felt as if he was being watched; as if the person who had written that shocking note was still around, mocking him. The thought of this blackmailer occupied his every waking moment and haunted Bermac's dreams.

One morning he awoke from one of these nightmares, drenched in sweat, to hear a crinkling sound which seemed to be coming from beneath his pillow. He felt around with his hand and soon withdrew a folded sheet of paper, and with trembling fingers he flattened it out in order to read its contents. In the pale morning light he squinted at the heart-stopping words and the nasty little drawing on that piece of paper. There was a crude sketch of a hanged man, and beside it a message which ran: 'Meet me at the West Façade of Notre Dame Cathedral at noon – murderer.'

Bermac trembled in his bed, consumed with mental anguish. He could not work out how the mysterious persecutor managed to get into his bedroom. He ran over and checked the door and soon found that he had forgotten to lock it. He could feel his heart thumping wildly in his chest; he had to get to the bottom of this business, the stress was killing him.

At noon, Roman Bermac loitered at the West Façade of Notre Dame Cathedral carrying a loaded pistol concealed in his inside coat pocket. A priest lingered near him for a while, smiling at him. Could this possibly be his tormenter in disguise? Never one to deliberate for long, Bermac reached for the gun, but fortunately for the priest, he moved away just at that moment and disappeared into the dense crowds milling around the cathedral, unaware of how close he had just come to being murdered. Bermac hung around the cathedral for a while, eyeing everyone with deep and murderous suspicion, but nobody else either approached him or showed the least interest in him.

The killer returned to his lodgings, gathered his belongings, and then moved on yet again to another squalid apartment, and once again he found a letter from the invisible blackmailer, this time telling him that his time was almost up. Snatching the note, Bermac stepped out on to his balcony and noticed a Neapolitan organ-grinder on the street below, smiling up at him, holding out his hat for change. Any sense of logic, or any connection with reality had long since deserted Bermac. On seeing the organ-grinder standing there he immediately jumped to the conclusion that he was the blackmailer.

"There's the culprit," he thought to himself. "Standing there with his hat outstretched! I'll teach him to mess with me. The swine!"

Seething with murderous rage, Bermac hurried down the stairs, smiled briefly back at the music maker, then, under the pretence of offering him a coin, knifed the man in the stomach in broad daylight and then casually strolled away, whistling to himself.

The police closed in further and Bermac was forced to flee the country, coming first to London and then travelling on to Liverpool, where he stayed at a lodging house in Everton. His intention was to board a ship to America as soon as possible. No sooner had Bermac started to unpack his belongings in Everton than something caught the corner of his eye. Filled with dread, he turned round to see an ominous-looking envelope propped up on the dressing table. It contained a note in that familiar taunting handwriting: 'Give yourself up, the game is over,' it stated in French.

Mr O'Neil, the lodging house deputy, happened to come into the room just moments after the discovery of the note, and Bermac pistol-whipped him across the face. However, this time he had met his match because O'Neil was an ex-boxer, and retaliated with a vicious upper-cut that floored the foreigner and left him sprawled unconscious on the floor.

Roman Bermac was taken to the Central Police Office at 111 Dale Street, where Chief Superintendent John Hancox interrogated him at length. Bermac confessed to the murder of the French businessman and the landlord, as well as to several other killings. He then ranted on about the tormentor who had been following him around, leaving him menacing letters. This was in the days before Freud of course, when Schizophrenia (a term first coined by the Swiss psychiatrist Eugene Bleuler in 1911) was known as dementia praecox. A detective who analysed the gloating letters found in Bermac's possession soon realised that there was something odd about them. The handwriting of these letters was exactly the same as Bermac's own. There was no doubt about it, the two scripts were indistinguishable.

Bermac was taken to Paris to answer for his murderous deeds, but he underwent serious mental deterioration en route, and ended up being committed to a lunatic asylum, where, it is alleged, numerous botched experimental operations were carried out on his brain.

Even in the locked solitary cell of the unhinged murderer, the teasing letters continued to appear – but crucially only when paper and pens were left with Bermac. This proved beyond doubt that the detective's theory was right – the dual-minded murderer had indeed penned the accursed letters himself, perhaps out of some deep-rooted subconscious guilt complex, or perhaps not. For who can pretend to understand the workings of a mind like Bermac's?

THE FACE CHANGER

We are not all the same. Most of us may belong to the same race they call Homo Sapiens, but I believe in the near future that Homo Superior – a new, better kind of human – will rear its head and render us as extinct as Neanderthal man. One only has to think of the dinosaurs – that reptilian dynasty which dominated the earth for 150 million years – until something catastrophic happened 65 million years ago and literally brought the reign of the monsters to an abrupt end, to realise how vulnerable we are to extinction. In comparison to the dinosaurs, the human being in its present form has only been around for 50,000 years, so who is to say how long we will remain in existence? I know for a fact that mutants are already living here among the human race, and these new variations of Homo Sapiens will, by the laws of nature, eventually replace the old model.

In the 1950s a secret survey was carried out in schools across England by the British Medical Council to analyse the IQ's of thousands of schoolchildren. Over a third of those tested had the intelligent quotient of a genius based on the test being used at the time, and the results of the study were so shocking that similar surveys were held in Europe and the United States – with the same outcomes. Scientists out forward the theory at the time that the isotope Strontium 90 – which did not exist in the atmosphere until Japan was atombombed in 1945 – had somehow improved the genetic makeup of children born in the late 1940s, endowing them with greater intellects than their predecessors. Is it possible that Strontium 90 in the genes could provide a rational explanation for the following strange fellow?

In 1966, a young man of about twenty-two years of age came out of Randles fish and chip shop on Smithdown Road. He stood by the Bendix Laundrette, eating his chips from their newspaper wrapping, when an elderly woman named

Joan Walsh, who was loading her laundry into a machine, noticed a young lady approach the youth. Joan looked back to her laundry, then a few moments later she heard a scream, and turned back to look through the window of the laundrette. The girl was hurrying away from the youth eating the chips – and that youth now had a completely different face. His nose was aquiline and his chin protruded, whereas before his nose had been much smaller and his chin quite rounded. Joan then watched as the man's face changed again before her very eyes. She came over all peculiar, and had to sit down on one of the benches. The young man with the sinister facial talent smiled at her, and nonchalantly continued eating his chips before walking off.

Joan's daughter related that eerie story to me, and was very surprised when I told her how the man with the changing face had also been reported in the Scotland Road area in 1967. Word of the incident only reached me in 2002 when an old listener to my spot on the *Billy Butler Show* telephoned me at the radio station. The caller, Ted Wilson, described how, as a young lad, he had been standing next to a youth as they both looked into the window of Vee's hardware store on Scotland Road in March 1967, when suddenly the youth turned to face him and asked: "Have you seen my eyes?" Ted went cold as he watched the lad's eyes turn from blue to black. The young man laughed at Ted's reaction, and then his entire face began to change. His features seemed to 'crawl' about his face and his nose extended, turned up, widened and changed into various shapes, along with his mouth and forehead. Ted Wilson was so petrified by the creepy metamorphosis that he ran off to find his father, who was drinking in the nearby Swann Inn pub, and his dad made the sign of the cross when his son related the strange tale, for Ted Wilson senior was convinced that the Devil was at large on Scotland Road.

Some people can contort their facial features into the most grotesque expressions; they call it 'gurning' and there are even competitions for it; but to change the colour of one's eyes and to completely alter the features of the face so that they bear no resemblance to the original visage is unheard of. A French actor by the name of Pierre Mes could 'will' his hair to stand on end whenever he chose, and no biologist has ever explained how he performed the 'trick'. I wonder if the 'face changer' of Scotland Road has any descendants who have inherited his unearthly talent for metamorphosis.

GREEN GHOST

T he mystery of the Green Ghost unfolded one hot Saturday afternoon in 1975 off Crown Street in the Edge Hill area of Liverpool. It all started when a seven-year-old boy called Raymond rushed into the Matlock pub in an agitated state and told his Uncle George that a "ghost man dressed in green" had just walked straight through the wall of the school. Uncle George momentarily glanced away from the *Grandstand* sports programme on the pub television, and simply said to Raymond: "Did it now? Run along and play now. That's a good lad."

No one else in the pub believed the child, and so Raymond ran back disappointed to the square of wasteland at the back of an advertisement hoarding on Crown Street, where his gang had built their den out of bits and pieces they had found lying around. The other three members of the gang – two boys, Alan and Joey and a girl named Marie – were fully expecting Raymond to return with his uncle. They had all seen the green ghost and they wanted an explanation for its amazing behaviour from an adult.

"He doesn't believe me," Raymond told them. "Too busy drinking and watching the stupid telly."

At that moment a snuffling noise was heard and Alan's dog, Vinny, squeezed into the secret hideout through a narrow gap between two pieces of corrugated iron, furiously wagging its tail. It had been Vinny that had first alerted the gang to the existence of the Green Ghost. The dog had been barking madly at something outside the den, and when the four kids went to find out what was going on, they had all seen the odd-looking man in the green velvet coat and the three-pointed hat, stooping to pick a wild flower from the ground in the middle of the wasteland, or 'oller' as the gang nicknamed it.

The stranger – who also wore a long fencing sword by his side – had ignored the children at first, being totally absorbed in what he was doing. A little later to stood up, stretched and started talking to them. The man seemed agitated and asked them repeatedly if they had seen a woman named Kitty. Marie asked the man to describe Kitty, and all he could say was that she had bright red hair. The children said they had seen no woman answering to that limited description in the area recently.

Plucking up courage, for there was definitely something strange about the man, Alan asked him who he was, and where he was from and how it was that he could walk through walls. The outlandishly dressed character revealed that his name was Mr Cornelius, and in a matter-of-fact way told them that he had been dead for about two hundred years! The children simply accepted everything he told them as the gospel truth, as young children do, and watched in delight as Mr Cornelius came and went through a section of the wall of a school on Olive Street.

The children all told their mothers and fathers and teachers about Mr Cornelius, but none of the adults took the slightest bit of notice, passing the story off as an innocent piece of make-believe – until an intriguing incident took place a week later. The children were playing in their den behind the hoarding one afternoon, when an old tramp squeezed through the opening in the wooden fence and roughly grabbed hold of Stephen, the youngest member of the gang, by the scruff of his neck. Seeing the assault, quick-witted Marie lost no time in running for help. She nimbly squeezed through a narrow gap in the corrugated iron which formed one side of the den, and ran as fast as her legs could carry her to her home on Smithdown Lane.

Within minutes, Marie's mother, father and grandmother had arrived at the children's den, and there they saw Mr Cornelius with their very own eyes. By the time they arrived, the aggressive tramp was nursing a deep cut to his forearm, apparently inflicted by the blade of Mr Cornelius's rapier. Minutes later, a policeman on his beat approached the den to see what all the trouble was about, and he arrested the tramp for the attempted abduction of one of the children. The plump old bobby apologised to Mr Cornelius, who was, after all, the hero of the hour, saying that he would have to accompany him to the station as well as the tramp. Taking the law into one's own hands was something he could not condone on his patch and he politely asked him to hand over his sword which was an offensive weapon and therefore illegal.

"Certainly not!" gasped Mr Cornelius and walked off tightly clutching his sword, seemingly without caring a fig for the fact that he had just been summoned to the police station. The policeman followed him, but before the constable could apprehend the quaintly dressed vigilante, he walked straight through a brick wall, leaving the officer of the law dumbstruck. Everyone – including the wounded tramp and Marie's parents and grandmother – stared in disbelief at the section of wall into which the ghost had vanished. It was completely intact and certainly contained no opening of any sort.

The phantom was allegedly seen several more times by the gang, and then turned up one day singing merrily to himself. He excitedly told the children that he had finally found Kitty Grimshaw, so they wouldn't be seeing him again. He said goodbye to the children, kissed Marie's hand and then said, "Remember me," before performing his usual vanishing act near the school wall.

After that eventful summer, the gang split up when they were all moved to different schools. The identities of the enigmatic Mr Cornelius and Kitty Grimshaw still remain a mystery to this day.

THE GREY LADY OF ALLERTON TOWER

One autumnal afternoon several years ago, whilst writing and researching a volume of *Haunted Liverpool*, I decided to take a much-needed break, having been hunched over my computer for most of the day. I set off for a walk which took me down Menlove Avenue, past Calderstone's Park and into another, almost deserted park, where I dwelt upon the gothic splendour of Allerton Tower's ruins. I strolled through the vestiges of the palatial home which I knew had once belonged to the illustrious Earle family; the magnificent remnants of a legendary grandiose residence, now sadly left to the mercy of the English weather, idiotic vandals and mindless graffiti 'artists'.

As I lingered near the shell of an outbuilding on the long-lost, seventy-eight-acre estate of Allerton Tower, something just glimpsed out the corner of my eye flitted past me. I half-turned reflexively, but the flitting 'thing' had vanished, leaving a sweet scent in its wake. I immediately wondered if the fabled Grey Lady of the ruins had just brushed past me. I certainly had not imagined that entity and it had not been a trick of the light. Some ghosts are quite timid, and manifest themselves so briefly that they come and go in the twinkling of an eye. The Grey Lady of the ruins has been seen by numerous witnesses over the years, and several years ago I was told the tragic story which lay behind the haunting of Allerton Tower.

In the 1850s, Sir Hardman Earle lived at Allerton Tower, along with his five daughters, Elizabeth, Mary, Harriet, Emily and Georgina, and his three troublesome sons, thirty-five-year-old Thomas, twenty-two-year-old Arthur and seventeen-year-old William. Sir Hardman Earle, a super-rich, highly-influential director of the Liverpool to Manchester Railway, and the person after whom Earlestown, in Newton-le-Willows, was named, harboured many dark secrets and skeletons in his cupboards, and some in the upper echelons of Lancashire society believed there were many controversial questions marks hanging over the source of Hardman's vast wealth.

One summer evening, the three Earle sons left the grounds of Allerton Tower on the pretext of taking an evening stroll, and without their father's knowledge, for he would have been furious had he known, they visited a local tavern in Woolton, where three local girls quickly fell for the wealthy trio. Thomas Earle had a wife at home, but periodically felt a craving which compelled him to go in search of the local maidens.

Upon this humid summer night, the three brothers went too far with their lustful desires, and in the deserted fields of Allerton, each of them ended up making love to the girls they had befriended at the tavern. Thomas and Arthur Earle were soon bidding their conquests a hasty goodnight after they'd taken their pleasure, but young intoxicated William, upon losing his virginity, was rashly declaring his intention to bring his lowly-born lover Mary home with him to meet their father. Upon hearing this preposterous suggestion, the two older brothers panicked and wrestled William away from the girl, then dragged him back home to Allerton Tower, where they tried everything in their power to quash all talk of infatuation.

However, William was not to be put off so easily and protested that he had fallen madly in love with his first conquest and that he was not prepared to abandon her, despite their protestations. From that day onwards, he seized every opportunity to sneak off from his father's sprawling mansion after dark to meet his beloved Mary; an Irish girl with beautiful blue eyes and long black hair. They became inseparable and planned to elope together, but somehow Sir Hardman Earle came to hear about the secret meetings and he gave his son a severe beating with his belt and had him confined to his rooms. The servants were given strict instructions to ensure that William stayed under lock and key. Sir Hardman also roundly criticised his older sons for leading young William astray.

Sometime afterwards, Mary was visited by Thomas Earle, who warned her to stay away from his teenaged brother, threatening her that if she knew what was good for her she would make sure she would never see him again. On hearing this, Mary began to cry bitterly, shyly confiding that she was already expecting William's child. Thomas was devastated by this new twist in the sad saga, realising that if word got out about the pregnancy it would create a scandal and bring shame on the whole family. Life at the Tower would not be worth living if that happened.

To make matters worse, the sobbing girl admitted that she had already told her Uncle Desmond about her condition, and he had immediately responded by saying that he would be going to visit Sir Hardman to demand some 'hush-money' to keep the disgraceful incident a secret. This latest admission made Thomas's blood run cold. How on earth had he let his brother fall into this trap from which there seemed to be no escape?

Thomas Earle returned to Allerton Tower and told no one about the news except his brother Arthur. They both understood that once blackmailers had got their teeth into their victims they would simply continue asking for more and more money, so the brothers decided on a drastic course of action. They would be forced to kill Mary and her uncle – there was no alternative.

One stormy night, young Mary was lured, unsuspecting, from her humble dilapidated home in Woolton Village by Thomas, the eldest of the Earle brothers, on the pretext that they needed to discuss the forthcoming birth of hers and William's child. She had received a note directing her to a secluded wood off a dirt track where Menlove Avenue now runs, and there she was ambushed and brutally bludgeoned to death by Thomas and Arthur Earle, who had been lying in wait for her. Arthur sobbed uncontrollably when he saw what he and his brother had done to the petite pregnant girl, but Thomas, who had inherited a greater measure of his father's ruthlessness, slapped him across the face and told him to stop his crying; their brother's welfare and the reputation of the Earle family was at stake. This was no time for regrets and faint heartedness, he argued, the girl was nothing but a slut, who deserved no better, and they had had no alternative but to kill her.

Arthur managed to compose himself sufficiently to help his brother carry the girl's limp and mangled body across a field at the far end of which they dropped it into the depths of an old well.

On the following evening, Desmond, the uncle of the murdered girl, was run down by a horse ridden by a man dressed in a long black cloak with a pulled-down hat-brim covering most of his face. Desmond died from his injuries several hours later without regaining consciousness. Then the body of Mary was hauled from the well, and most people assumed that she had accidentally fallen to her death, because the well had no protective wall around it, whilst others quickly suspected foul play, arguing that the two deaths, on consecutive nights, simply could not be put down to coincidence.

Some gypsy families were living in the area at the time, and Sir Hardman Earle suspected that they might have something to do with Mary's death, but one of the Romany men, whose surname was Wryme, eager to rid his community of suspicion, declared that he would be able to locate and identify the murderer of the Irish girl by the use of a divining rod. Soon afterwards, Wryme, followed by an assorted crowd of curious locals, assembled at the well where Mary's body had been discovered. He walked from the well with the dowsing rod in his hands pointing the way. The rod noticeably twitched up and down several times, and, to the delight of the onlookers, Wryme would occasionally spit out blood as he picked up the psychic scent of the killer. The gypsy walked in a straight line across the waterlogged fields of Woolton, with the crowds of sensation seekers growing behind him as he moved northwards from the well. Then Wryme's hands began to tremble violently as the rod reacted to something, and a wave of gasps coursed through the crowd as the Romany dowser approached Allerton Tower.

Two gardeners on the Earle estate tried to stop Wryme and the crowd, telling them that they were trespassing on private land, but the mob ignored him and crushed forward, determined to pursue the chase to the end; they hadn't enjoyed so much free entertainment since the last Sunday School outing. Before long Wryme reached the entrance to the Orangery of the colossal mansion, where he came face to face with the imperious figure of Sir Hardman Earle. When Wryme explained what he was doing, Sir Hardman became outraged. He turned on his heels, his whiskers bristling with indignation, and went to fetch several servants, also bringing with him two loaded pistols. The mob slowly began to disperse at the sight of the pistols and reluctantly started to walk back the way they had come. When Sir Hardman fired a pistol shot in the air as a warning, the retreat turned into a stampede; the locals being only too well aware of His Lordship's ruthless reputation.

But that was not the end of the matter. Some weeks later, the male members of the Hardman family began to reap the consequences of their terrible actions when the apparition of a beautiful, pale-faced girl with bedraggled wet hair and soaking wet clothes appeared first in the bedroom of Thomas Earle. She brought with her the weight of immeasurable sadness which seemed to fill the room and her ghost looked so solid, that Thomas felt he could reach out and touch it. He could even see water dripping off it on to the carpet. He wrung his hands and screamed out in terror, upon which the girl, whom he recognised at once as his brother's sweetheart whom he had so savagely murdered, vanished into the night air.

Shortly afterwards, Arthur Earle was also visited by the dripping phantom. She appeared at his bedside at four o'clock in the morning. This time the girl's ghost was groaning in agony from the terrible wounds to her head and body and with a steady gaze, pointed an accusing finger at Arthur. By the time she had disappeared he had been reduced to a jibbering wreck and would never enjoy a peaceful night's sleep again.

The spectre persecuted the two brothers for many years, and was also said to have made an appearance of a more benign kind before her lover William Earle when he was a soldier, in 1885, on the eve of his death in the Sudan. She had also appeared to his father, Sir Hardman Earle, as he lay on his deathbed in 1877.

Since that time, the ghost of the murder victim has been seen on many occasions treading forlornly among the ruins of Allerton Tower, and she is now known as the Grey Lady of Allerton Tower.

HAUNTED OFFICE BLOCK

In the 1990s, at a certain office block in Liverpool city centre, a woman in her twenties named Julia was taken on as a female security guard. She usually worked with a colleague named Stuart, and on one windy night, she arrived at the office block to work the 11pm till 7am shift. The office block was empty except for Julia and Stuart, and after closing and locking the entrance doors, the alarms were armed, and the two of them settled down at the reception desk. The long monotonous hours of the night would be punctuated by the mandatory hourly patrols of the building, as well as episodes of chit-chat, crossword puzzles, and listening to the radio.

Upon this particular night, at a quarter-past eleven, Stuart received a telephone call from his brother-in-law which drained his face of colour. Stuart's sister had been critically injured in a car crash on Edge Lane, and had been rushed to the Royal Liverpool Hospital on Prescot Street. Stuart asked Julia if he could go to the hospital at once, and without thinking for a minute, Julia said she'd be fine on her own. This was an emergency after all, so the alarms were deactivated and Stuart grabbed his car keys and ran out of the building to the car park. Within ten minutes he was at the hospital at his sister's bedside.

Meanwhile, back at the office block, Julia had resecured all the doors, turned the alarm back on, and set off on her first round of the building. She went up in the elevator, and walked the dark corridors that were illuminated only by her flashlight and the luminance filtering through the windows from the streetlamps of the city outside. She opened a set of large impressive doors and looked into the boardroom. Her flashlight bounced off the polished mahogany furniture; nothing amiss there. She checked the boss's plush office along with several other rooms, then walked down the stairwell to the next level, and inspected each of the rooms down there, and so on.

About twenty-five minutes later, having completed her tour of inspection, she was heading back down to the reception area of the building, her mind occupied with troubled thoughts about Stuart's sister. The elevator doors suddenly parted, which was unusual and Julia crossed over to the three-sided reception counter. Something unusual then caught her eye in the book which all employees and security personnel had to sign when they entered and left the building and which was lying open on the counter. On a blank page, there was a drawing in biro of a smiley face with a pair of horns. That drawing had definitely not been there when Stuart and Julia had signed the book earlier at the start of their shift – they would have commented on it. She could also have sworn that the logbook had been closed when she had set out on her rounds. There was only one obvious logical conclusion; there was an intruder in the building.

Just at the edge of Julia's vision something was blinking. She turned and saw that it was the floor indicators of the elevator console. The red light on the console was slowly rising up the column of indicators, to the top floor, as if someone had just summoned the elevator. The topmost light winked on, then after a long pause, it started to descend. The elevator was coming down again and she had to assume that the intruder was inside. Neither she nor Stuart was allowed to take any weapons into work with which to tackle an intruder, or for protection. She looked around for something with which to defend herself and spotted a heavy ashtray stand in the reception area. She rushed over and grabbed it firmly in both hands. It would make a formidable club in the event of an attack, but what if the intruder was carrying a knife, or even a gun?

After what seemed like an age, the elevator reached the ground floor and the sound of its bell echoed through the deserted office block. Oh why did this have to happen on a night when she was on her own? thought Julia.

The door opened.

Her heart thumping, Julia stood to the side of the reception counter, waiting for someone to emerge from the elevator. No one did. After a while she plucked up the courage to walk across the carpeted room to the elevator. She looked inside and confirmed that there was no one hiding there. Suddenly, the image of the horned smiley face came back into her mind. How had it got there? Was it possible that Stuart had been doodling in the logbook just before he left and she hadn't noticed? Julia wondered. She soon dismissed that possibility. It was so out of character he took his job very seriously, and she was certain he hadn't scribbled that face. He wasn't the sort who doodled, especially in something as important as the logbook, and she was still certain that the logbook had been closed when she had commenced her rounds.

The elevator door closed slowly once more and this time it stayed put on the ground floor. Julia stood there uneasily, still clutching the ash tray, with a jumble of confused thoughts jangling through her head, when she was startled by the ringing of the telephone in the reception area. She dashed to the phone and grabbed the receiver; at the other end of the line she could hear Stuart crying. Through his sobs he told her that his sister had been put on the critical list. She had multiple injuries and it was touch and go whether she would survive the night.

"I'll be back as soon as I can," Stuart told Julia. "I can't leave you to do the shift on your own."

"No, don't be silly, Stuart," said Julia, trying to keep the fear out of her voice. "Your place is at the hospital with your sister. I'll be absolutely fine on my own. I'll be thinking of you."

"Well, if you're sure. I really don't want to leave her," said Stuart falteringly.

"Of course not. I'll see you when I see you. Off you go."

"Thanks, Julia. I owe you one."

Stuart then hung up.

Just before four in the morning, Julia was listening to the radio turned on at low volume. Her nerves had just about returned to normal but her ears were pricked for the least sound. Suddenly, she thought she heard a sound somewhere in the heart of the building. She thumbed the volume control and muted the radio, then listened intently, every nerve in her body strained and tense. Someone was whistling. It seemed to echo faintly down the stairs, and it sent shivers of dread down Julia's spine. She crept over to the heavy fire door that led to the stairwell, and noticed that the whistling was now slightly louder. The tune seemed vaguely familiar but she couldn't quite place it – then suddenly she recognised the eerie melody. It was a song she had not heard since she was a child, way back in the 1970s. It was *Moonshadow* by Cat Stevens.

"Who's there?" Julia shouted up the pitch-black stairwell.

Her voice echoed up the stairs and was swallowed up in the darkness and no reply came. The whistling faded, then came a brief distant chuckle of laughter. She swept the beam of her torch across the underside of the concrete steps that turned and spiralled convolutedly in a vertical direction overhead. There was no one there that she could make out, no movement of any kind.

The telephone in the reception area rang out again. Julia spun round and hurried towards it with dark forebodings. This was turning out to be one heck of a night. Would it be bad news from Stuart? She lifted the receiver and waited for his voice. Silence. Not even the sound of any background noise in the hospital.

"Hello?" Julia said, still expecting to hear Stuart, but instead detecting a faint chuckling.

"Who is that?" she asked, and she looked over her shoulder uneasily as the sniggering sound continued.

It stopped after about ten seconds, followed by a telephonic dead tone. Julia replaced the receiver, and tried her utmost not to let the strange events of the night get the better of her, but just as she was regaining a measure of composure, one of the internal phones started to ring. Julia answered it – only to be met with dead silence, just as before, but no faint laughter this time. The silence went on for something like a minute in total, after which Julia slammed the receiver down, feeling that someone was playing tricks with her.

Although she was decidedly anxious by now, what with the mysterious doodler, the sinister whistler and the telephone pest, Julia was a gutsy woman and was determined to get to the bottom of all the nocturnal disturbances. Of course, the thought of the culprit being a ghost did cross her mind several times, but Julia had always been a down-to-earth woman who had no time for such 'figments' of the human imagination, a fact which had made her so suitable for the job in the first place.

"There are no such things as ghosts," she muttered to herself over and over again like a mantra.

Then all the lights in the reception went out.

Julia barged forward over the counter, fumbling for the flashlight, knocking over Stuart's empty mug as she did so. It rolled off the ledge behind the counter and shattered and the sound seemed to fill the entire reception area. Her hand searched for Stuart's MagLite torch and switched that on too. She then proceeded to the small metal door set in the wall opposite the entrance. She unlocked it and opened it – and saw at once that the emergency power supply to the alarms wasn't on. There should have been two steadily glowing red auxiliary power indicators there, but the console was completely dark. That seemed impossible, because the alarm system to that tower block had its own battery. Julia swore under her breath and tried clicking switches and turning keys in the console, but it seemed as if there wasn't an amp of power left in the system.

She read the emergency call-out number on the inside of the door of the alarm unit, then repeated it to herself as she went to the telephone. Although it was nigh on five in the morning, an electrician would surely be on call to service the alarm and hopefully to diagnose the cause of the electricity failure throughout the office block. Julia picked up the phone and dialled the 0800 number – but the phone sounded dead. She dialled again. The phone was definitely dead.

It was at that moment that she noticed some dark unfamiliar object standing over by the fire door. What on earth was it? Julia swore under her breath with fright. It was silhouetted, about four feet high and broad, with a flattened top. Julia shone the two torches directly at the thing, and they illuminated a truly grotesque spectacle. Caught in the beams of the torches was a hideously disfigured man. The top of his bald head was as flat as a pancake and the head itself was partly embedded into his chest, so that only his face from the nose up was visible, and the tops of his legs were hidden somewhere in the upper abdomen. His arms were of normal length in proportion to this compacted, squashed together torso, yet the hands were almost scraping the floor. It looked as if this poor individual had sustained horrific injuries from some major accident, yet Julia realised that no person could survive being crushed and maimed in such a way and still survive.

The compressed figure toddled silently towards Julia on its stumpy legs, and she let out a scream which seemed to reverberate around the whole building. All her instincts told her to get out, to escape this nightmare, and she wheeled round to make for the entrance of the building – but she'd left the keys in the recess behind the door of the alarm unit, right on the other side of the room. In sheer desperation she pulled repeatedly at the handles of the doors, but they wouldn't budge, and then with shuddering revulsion she felt the clammy hands of the grossly misshapen man groping her legs and her bottom.

Still screaming, she careered off in a curve which eventually took her back to the alarm console, where she searched frantically for the keys to the entrance doors. Faltering footsteps echoed in the foyer as the ghastly deformed intruder staggered inexorably towards her, sniggering like something possessed – that very same sniggering she had heard earlier on the telephone.

After fumbling around for what seemed like an age, Julia suddenly located the keys, grabbed them, and ran around the reception counters to the entrance doors, with the hideous loping thing in close pursuit. She turned the key in the lock and pulled it open just in time to avoid another encounter with those clammy hands. She fled out into the windy street. The clouds had parted with the gales and a waning gibbous moon shone down on the deserted streets. Julia sped off as fast as her legs would carry her, deserting her duty, and looking back only once to confirm that she had finally shaken off the repulsive squashed-together figure.

Not surprisingly, after the experiences of that night she refused to set foot in that building ever again. She had thought that she was cut out for the job but not any more; she would be looking for something much more sedate, perhaps in an office, and definitely during daylight hours.

A week later, when Stuart's sister was taken off the critical list, Julia visited her at the Royal Hospital and was pleased to find Stuart by her bedside looking and sounding much more hopeful for her complete recovery. After the visit, she related to him the events of that terrible night and described the weird-looking man with the hideous-looking body. He apologised for not having been there and told her that he had heard an old ghost story about a man who had been horrifically killed in a freak accident in the office block while it was being built in the 1970s, perhaps it was his ghost, it certainly sounded like it.

Apparently, the man, an electrician, had been working in the elevator shaft when two of his colleagues boarded the elevator without realising that he was in the shaft and sent it down to the ground floor. The electrician had no chance of escape and was crushed to death by the descending elevator, and when his body was recovered, the head had been squashed into the chest, and the force of the impact had pushed his thighs right up into his abdomen. There was a rumour that the accident victim had still been alive when he was hoisted up the shaft, and that his eyes were bulging so wide with shock that they were nearly out of their sockets. Having been set down on the floor outside the elevator, he had tried to run from the building, but after a few feet had fallen down and died on the spot.

After the office block was officially opened, the night workers often heard the ghost of the man whistling all over the building, and sometimes even glimpsed his apparition standing in corridors. The management of the building tried to hush up these weird rumours, but the ghost was still occasionally seen at large, at all hours of the morning, and with the most nerve-shattering activity taking place each year on the anniversary of the tragic accident. Sometimes strange graffiti would be scrawled on the walls of the stairwell and even in the log book. The ghost had even been known to play havoc with the telephone and alarm systems …

Julia shuddered upon hearing all of this, because when the alarm engineer was called out later that morning, she heard that he had found nothing amiss; the electricity was fully on and the alarm system was functioning perfectly.

The office block still stands today, and from time to time I still hear about strange goings-on in the premises.

THE JUBILEE PLOT

No one in Everton's Orient Street was prepared to believe Mrs McGowan's far-fetched tale, in which she claimed that her Liverpool-Irish cousin had been framed by the British Government. All the reports in the newspapers about the lads trying to blow up Queen Victoria were pure hogwash, according to Mary McGowan, and what's more, the people who had really planted the dynamite under the throne of the Monarch were not the Fenians, but the British Government itself!

Even Ann Richards, a neighbour and lifelong friend of Mary McGowan's, couldn't help but smirk at the outrageous assertion. Who ever heard of such nonsense? The local scripture reader and religious fanatic John Armstrong, who lived several doors away from Mary, also heard of her incredible tale, and paid her a visit to deliver a personal sermon on the evils of spreading treasonous lies. At the time he called, Mary was upstairs making beds and tidying the bedrooms. She heard the doorbell ring and looked out of the front bedroom window to check who was there. Seeing the indignant preacher poised, foot tapping, ready for one of his tedious sermons, and guessing what the subject would be about, Mary promptly emptied the contents of a chamberpot over him from the upstairs window.

The preacher probably wasn't too surprised by this turn of events, because Mary McGowan had retaliated in a similarly aggressive way earlier in the month when Armstrong had actually managed to gain entry to her house. On this occasion the purpose of his visit had been to try and stop her from dabbling in the 'Black Art' of tea-leaf reading, for which she had quite a formidable reputation in the neighbourhood.

All of this took place in 1888, the year after the so-called Jubilee Plot. Incredible as it may seem, Mary McGowan was right; the British Government was indeed responsible for placing dynamite under the throne of Queen Victoria at Westminster Abbey. Let me explain.

In 1858 a revolutionary movement called the Fenians, who demanded Home Rule for Ireland, was born simultaneously in both New York and Dublin. In the 1880s, the Fenians launched an all out bombing campaign on mainland Britain to draw attention to their cause, and it was rumoured that even Buckingham Palace and Windsor Castle would soon be targeted.

In June 1887, three Fenians boarded the *SS City of Chester* at New York and set sail for Liverpool. Concealed in their trunks they carried three Smith & Wesson revolvers and several boxes of ammunition. In addition, sewn into the trios clothing, was over one hundred pounds of powerful Atlas Dynamite Powder from Philadelphia. The mission of these so-called Dynamitards was to blow up Queen Victoria, along with the British Government, during the forthcoming Jubilee thanksgiving service at Westminster Abbey, and so change the course of history.

In the event, the Fenians arrived several days too late at Liverpool to execute their plan and so, angry and frustrated, they melted into the crowds at the docks, unaware that they were being closely observed by British Intelligence agents, and completely oblivious to the fact that they had been set up. This was hardly surprising, for how could they possibly have predicted that the British Government itself would have secretly financed this potential mass murder of the Monarchy and its entire Cabinet?

On the sunny morning of 21 June 1887, the Royal procession swept through the gates of Buckingham Palace and threaded its way through a route lined with loyal subjects and cheering flag-wavers, bound for the thanksgiving service at Westminster Abbey. When she arrived at her destination, Queen Victoria, as usual, cut a severe and dignified figure, seated upon the ancient regal seat of Edward the Confessor. There were to be no explosions to mar the splendour of that day's pomp and ceremony and everything passed off perfectly according to plan. Her Majesty had been saved in the nick of time from the gravest danger – or so the British people were led to believe.

The Jubilee bombers were swiftly rounded up and sentenced to penal servitude for life and within a short space of time they were linked by several letters to Mr Charles Parnell and other Irish MPs who had been campaigning for Home Rule. The letters – all of which were reprinted in the National Press – were bogus, of course, and the man who forged them was later unmasked, and he subsequently committed suicide. It also turned out that the dynamite found stashed under the throne at Westminster Abbey had not been planted there by the Liverpool-Irish bombers after all. Indeed, it was later established that it had actually been purchased by British Intelligence agents and that it was they who had planted it there.

The whole outrageous plot – dreamed up in the top-secret Room 56 at the Home Office – was designed and carried out with the sole purpose of discrediting the Fenians and Irish Home Rule MP Charles Parnell, although he later successfully sued a national newspaper for five thousand pounds in libel damages over the affair. Queen Victoria profusely thanked the Prime Minister Lord Salisbury for saving her life, quite unaware that it was he who had actually masterminded the Jubilee Plot!

For some reason, Mary McGowan was aware of all this back in 1888, but no one was prepared to believe her, and the intrigue was not cleared up until the top secret information relating to the notorious Jubilee plot was declassified in the year 2000, and was found to corroborate her story.

MAY QUEEN

One beautiful warm sunny Saturday of 30 April 1892, twelve-year-old Rosetta Williams from Liverpool was picnicking with her recently widowed mother on a hill near the Delamere Forest when she became aware of strange ethereal voices being carried on the wind. The whisperings of her name sounded like far-off children playing, and the golden-haired girl looked about her, smiling, and blinking with amazement, unable to get a fix on the direction from which the ghostly sounds were coming. Rosetta's mother, reclining on the picnic blanket soaking up the April sunshine, could hear nothing beyond the gentle lazy drone of an occasional bumble bee and the wind soughing through the trees, and she drowsily told her daughter that she must be imagining things. After quite a while, the voices slowly faded away into the forest as mysteriously as they had first come to Rosetta's notice.

At about four o'clock a sharp chill suddenly pervaded the air, reminding them that it was still only early in the year and it brought the picnic to an abrupt end. Mrs Williams packed up the remaining sandwiches, apples and half-full bottle of dandelion wine into the picnic basket and set off for the cottage of her Welsh mother, Megan, with Rosetta trailing behind, picking wildflowers and listening to the songs of the wild birds. Ever since the funeral of her husband back in Liverpool, Mrs Williams had been trying to get her bearings again in this quiet little haven. She was still deeply uncertain about her future without he husband Jonathan, and she felt she was too old to remarry, despite her mother's reassurances that she would find another good husband one day.

On the following morning, Rosetta came smiling down to the breakfast table, wearing an elaborate crown, fashioned from a hundred intertwined daisies or more, on her head. However, her beaming smile was quickly wiped clean off her face by a shriek of alarm from her grandmother.

"Where did you get that thing?" asked Megan, stuffing a trembling hand to her mouth.

"You're never going to believe this, Grandma, but I found it on the bedside table when I woke up this morning," the girl told her. "Do you think Mama put it there for me to find?"

Grandma Megan told her to take it off and throw it outside at once, but Rosetta said the crown was much too beautiful to be thrown away, and flatly refused to take it off.

"Throw it away, child!" Megan ordered her, and tried to snatch the crown from the girl's head.

"No, I will not!" protested Rosetta, upset by her grandmother's unusual burst of temper. "It's beautiful and I shall wear it."

Her mother then came to the table and reprimanded her daughter for showing such disrespect and insolence towards her grandmother, and she told the child to do as she was told and throw the crown away at once. Rosetta stormed out of the cottage in a huff, still wearing the crown, and ran off deep into the forest. She cried until she had no tears left and wished with all her heart that her father was alive – he would understand.

Lost in thought, Rosetta followed a number of different paths and trails for quite a distance until she came upon a sunny clearing in the ancient forest, in the middle of which was a perfect circle of smooth, randomly-sized stones bordered with wild flowers of every colour. A strange atmosphere of joyous expectation hung in the air in this place; a feeling that was impossible to account for, but which reminded her of the sweet voices she had heard the previous day. Delicate sweet aromas filled the air, and Rosetta suddenly had the feeling that she was not alone, but she didn't feel at all frightened.

Suddenly she was overcome by an uncanny urge to skip around the stone circle, and as she did so, she felt so unaccountably happy; that she could have stayed there forever. She started to sing as she skipped and danced around the circle and she was accompanied by the sweetest pipe music coming from nowhere in particular.

Back at the cottage, Mrs Williams and her mother became frantic with worry about Rosetta when she didn't return after a few hours. They searched all the usual forest trails and paths but all in vain, there was no sign of her. Eventually, they had no alternative but to return to the cottage, both burdened with anxiety for the child. Megan was consumed with guilt; she should never have scolded her in that way. How was the child supposed to understand the terrible significance of that daisy wreath? She was convinced that she had been responsible for driving her away. She realised that times hadn't been easy recently with the death of the child's father and she should have behaved more sensitively.

Mrs Williams and her mother sat tearfully in front of the fire, which by this time had fallen low, neither woman even noticing the increasing chill which had pervaded the cottage. The silver-tongued clock on the mantelpiece chimed the hour of seven, shaking them out of their inertia and Mrs Williams decided to go and report her daughter's absence to the policeman in the local village. Perhaps he would help them get up a search party.

Moments after her departure, Megan decided to pay one last visit to Delamere Forest in an effort to find Rosetta. She was to behold an alarming sight which would confirm all her worst suspicions. The old woman walked deep into the woodland until she was stopped in her tracks by the sound of voices and singing. She crept up to the edge of a clearing and there she saw some thirty men, women and children from the local village. All of them were dancing merrily around the circle of stones at the centre of the clearing, and sitting in the middle of them all was Rosetta, wearing an even more elaborate daisy crown, and nothing more than a flimsy silk garment which was not her own. She looked groggy, as if the villagers had plied her with cider or strong beer. The superstitious locals had obviously chosen golden-haired Rosetta as their sacred May Queen. Without a second thought, Megan broke into the circle of frenzied dancers and made her way to Rosetta who looked at her with unknowing eyes. Her grandmother shook her to her senses and then battled back through the circle of inebriated revellers and dragged Rosetta, stumbling, back to the cottage.

Rosetta's mother and an old policeman were just about to go looking for Megan and her granddaughter, having just checked the cottage to make sure that the child had not returned. When Mrs Williams saw her bruised and scratched mother and the drunken Rosetta, she was alarmed and confused, until Megan explained how every year at the end of April, the locals chose the May Queen, alternately known as the Flower Bride and the Lady of the Faeries. Megan earnestly tried to explain how it was the 'little people' who were behind it all, and how they sometimes abducted girls for the ceremony. Chillingly, those girls were never seen again! Megan urged her daughter to return to Liverpool with Rosetta immediately, for it would definitely not be safe for them to stay at the cottage for the rest of that night. There would be certain to be reprisals for breaking up this important Mayday ceremony and they might well come looking for her.

Mrs Williams took her mother's advice seriously but unfortunately they had missed the last train to Liverpool and so she and her daughter could not make it back home that night. They were forced to stay at the cottage, whose windows and doors were all barred and bolted, and throughout that night the house was besieged by all kinds of weird phenomena. Coloured lights danced about like fireflies outside the windows and there were strange raps on the windowpanes and doors. Cackling laughter was heard up the chimney and some of the frustrated villagers stood outside the cottage for most of the night, creating a terrible racket by banging pots and pans and screeching.

Mrs Williams and her daughter were relieved and thankful to return, unharmed, to Liverpool by train the following morning. Perhaps the countryside wasn't quite such a peaceful place after all!

THE PAWNBROKER'S MOTH

I love stories where the fate or fortune of an individual turns on some little incident that seems trifling and insignificant at the time. This tale, from Victorian Liverpool, was first told to me as a child by my grandmother. She heard the story from her own mother, who once lived near Richmond Row, the scene of so many fascinating goings-on at that time.

One blisteringly hot sunny Saturday afternoon in May 1894, a poor ten-year-old girl named Molly Hewson left her ramshackle home at Number 10 Devon Street in the north-end of Liverpool, and walked barefoot over the hot flags, singing to herself. Times had been very hard since her mother had died a year ago. Like many men in his situation, her father had been unable to cope with his wife's death and had turned to drink. Her older sister had left home to live with her boyfriend, just to escape the beatings and the endless drunken scenes, leaving poor Molly to bear the brunt of her father's drunkenness and violence.

Upon this fine afternoon it was a great relief for Molly to be able to escape from the draughty cold house and her inebriated, violent father. Without a penny to her name, the girl skipped up Soho Street, where a little scrawny black mongrel dog started to follow her. She was lucky to have inherited her mother's happy disposition and could always find something to smile about. She and her new-found friend crossed over Richmond Row and headed north into the busy thoroughfare of Great Homer Street. Molly loved to look in the windows of the shops on this popular street, which was even more crowded than usual upon this weekend afternoon. In those days you could buy practically anything you wanted in those shops, providing you had the money. For Molly, just looking was enough.

Mr Smith the butcher came out of his shop wearing his straw boater and jolly red striped apron, and kindly handed a little bone to the unnamed dog which Molly had adopted. The dog trotted on after the barefoot girl with the bone between his narrow, clenched jaws and his tail wagging. Molly looked in the window of George Sturla's Pawnbroker's shop at the myriad selection of objects on display. This was one of her favourite shops because you never knew what would be in the window from one day to the next; the objects on display changed on an almost daily basis. But on this occasion, Molly was looking for one thing in particular. Yes! There he was again, the little golden butterfly with the purple-bordered wings. Molly had had her eye on that butterfly for the last couple of days and she lightly tapped her finger on the window pane and he fluttered on to a dusty old ornate clock. The girl went into the shop and asked Mr Sturla how much was the butterfly in the window.

"Well, if you will mop up here I will let you have it for nothing," he said.

"Thanks, Mr Sturla," Molly nodded, wide-eyed and smiling.

She diligently mopped up the floor of the shop as her dog grappled with the bone outside.

When she had finished the job, Mr Sturla told her that she could pick any of the toys on display in the window as a reward, but Molly insisted that all she wanted was the butterfly, so the pawnbroker put it in a jar and screwed on the lid into which he had pierced several holes. He also gave the girl twopence for cleaning his floor. Molly walked in a daze of delight out of the shop, gazing at the beautifully coloured insect in the jar, hardly able to believe that she had him at last. As she reached the junction of Richmond Row, a dirty-faced street urchin tapped her on the shoulder, and when Molly turned to see who it was, the boy lurched forward and grabbed the jar from her. He grinned a smile of missing and blackened teeth as he held the jar close up to his eyes and shook it.

"What have you got here then?" he said, and seeing it was a live butterfly, he told Molly he was going to smash the jar in the road.

"Give it back. It's mine," said Molly, bursting into tears.

Then, all of a sudden, an elderly man who had been passing by hooked the handle of his walking cane around the urchin's neck and the struggling boy was hauled towards him. The old man grabbed the jar from the ragged boy's hands and he ran off rubbing his neck and muttering curses to himself.

"Oh! Thank you so much for getting my butterfly back, sir," said Molly, wringing her hands.

"My word!" gasped the man, gazing at the jar. "That's not a butterfly, it's a moth and a very rare moth into the bargain! Epione Parallelaria! The Dark-bordered Beauty Moth!" he said, looking as if he was going to faint.

The old man was James McLaughlin, a brilliant lepidopterist (a man who studied moths and butterflies) and in all of his seventy years he had never come across a specimen such as this one before. Without hesitation he dipped into his waistcoat pocket and pulled out a half sovereign and purchased that moth from Molly. In addition, he promised her that she could visit him every day at Number

9 Richmond Row, where he kept his vast collection of moths and butterflies.

The rest of the story almost runs like a fairytale. Molly took up the kind stranger's invitation and soon became a frequent visitor at James McLaughlin's comfortable home. There she was introduced to the fascinating creatures in his collection, which came in all shapes, sizes and colours, and McLaughlin found her a willing and able pupil; someone to share the passion he felt for his life's work. He soon became very fond of the child and when her father passed away two months later, McLaughlin had no hesitation in adopting Molly and she later married his grandson.

THE RUNCORN DRAGON

In 1821, the writer Heinrich Heine stated: "Where they burn books, they will end in burning human beings." Just over a century afterwards, the Nazis did exactly that.

Going centuries further back in time, the Apostle Paul supervised the burning of all the 'strange books' on the occult at Ephesus, and earlier than this, in 47 BC, we have the most famous general in history, Julius Caesar, burning scrolls of ancient knowledge at the Great Library of Alexandria.

In the long history of human stupidity, mountains of books and papyrus scrolls containing information on the lost secret wisdom of the ancients have been burned in orgies of insanity, fanaticism and religious fervour. All that remains of some of these incinerated manuscripts of old are legends, transmitted by the spoken word, and the following tale is derived from such folklore.

After the Roman withdrawal from Britain in the fifth century, there were many further invasions. Norsemen and Danes and Saxons arrived in waves on to our shores, and in those times of bloodshed and troubles, King Vortigern of Britain fled to Wales during one of the battles and was later murdered. In the wars that followed, a man named Arthur arose to lead the Britons in battle against the marauding Saxons and other invaders, and he later became the Over King of Britain. The rest, of course, is history: the rise and fall of Camelot, the tragic disbandment of the one hundred and fifty Knights of the Round Table, and the banishment of Merlin at Alderley Edge in Cheshire.

The 'Once and Future King' died around 537 AD, and was transported by boat from the Wirral peninsula to the Isle of Man, known to the ancient Celts as the Isle of Avalon. Wirral at that time was largely covered in thick forest, and parts of it were owned by Arthur's nephew, Sir Gawain.

When the boat returned from Avalon, one of the pallbearers, a mystical Mercian knight named Jareen, was summoned to a village close to where modern Runcorn now exists. A dragon known as the Morgawr (pronounced 'Morgwer') was terrorising the villagers and carrying off their sheep and cattle to its lair in a cave on the banks of the Mersey. Sir Jareen and his faithful muscular Great Dane – which was always clad in spiked armour – arrived at the village to see what could be done to help. The knight could smell the strong smell of burning long before he could actually see the village. He found a farmstead ablaze and the blackened charred corpses of soldiers who had tried to fight off Morgawr scattered all about.

Sir Jareen had a formidable reputation as a man of action and he lost no time in formulating a plan to rid the village of the dragon. He quickly rallied round the dazed survivors and encouraged them to dig a hole in a field close to the village. Next to the pit, five plump sheep were tethered to a post. The hole was completely covered with a lattice of thin wooden slats and canvas, and carefully camouflaged with leaves and branches, so that from above it could not be seen. Sir Jareen then hid in the bottom of the pit beneath the canvas, in his full battle armour, with his double-edged sword at the ready.

As the sun was setting and turning the horizon crimson and gold, an ominous dark silhouette appeared in the sky, and although it was some distance away, the flapping of its gigantic wings was clearly audible. It was the mighty Morgawr, and within minutes it was circling the village, uttering dreadful cries and blasting the air with foul-smelling gouts of methane gas. In seconds the village streets were empty, the ordinary people barricading themselves indoors and falling to their knees in prayer.

The dragon quickly spied the drove of sheep and dived through the air to seize them as an appetiser. Jareen felt the ground shudder as the enormous beast came in to land, and he pulled away a small section of the canvas cover and saw that he was directly beneath the vast heaving belly of the beast. He rammed his sword repeatedly through the scaly flesh of the dragon's underbelly and the Morgawr's deafening groans thundered round the village. Torrents of sticky red blood quickly began to fill the pit and Jareen was almost drowned in the deluge of gore, but he just managed to squeeze out of the pit in time, between the earthen ridge of the hole and the scaly underside of the dragon.

Back above ground he was met by a terrifying sight. His armoured Great Dane, Brennos, was savaging the head of the dragon, while successive torrents of flame narrowly missed the surviving sheep and incinerated all the trees surrounding the pit. Picking his moment very carefully, Sir Jareen leapt between the thrashing limbs of the wounded beast and thrust his sword between the Morgawr's eyes, upon which the flames immediately ceased and the creature rolled over in its final death throes.

A cheer went up from the joyous villagers who slowly emerged from their hideaways one by one when they realised that the accursed dragon was no more. There was much feasting that night, but for Sir Jareen and Brennos the dragon slaying was all in a day's work. They did not linger to bask in the glory of their amazing feat, but were soon on the road again, in search of other daring adventures.

Since the dawn of recorded history, dragons have been reported, in ancient texts found in Babylon, Assyria, Greece, China, Africa, America and Japan. Classical writers such as Pliny and Aristotle both claimed that dragons had once existed.

Upon several island in Indonesia, the fierce-looking Komodo dragons, giant lizards that can grow up to ten feet in length, are still to be found. Of course, they can't fly and they don't breathe fire, but perhaps such a creature did exist once in prehistoric times, co-existing with Tyrannosaurus Rex and the Pterodactyl, and it is just possible that an isolated pocket of them did manage to survive the worldwide extinction of the dinosaurs.

Could these hypothetical creatures be responsible for the global legends of the dragon?

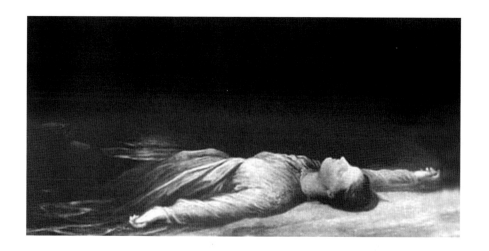

TWO MARITIME GHOSTS

One blisteringly hot summer afternoon on Southport beach in 1976, Chris and Jan, a young holidaymaking Liverpool couple in their twenties, were sitting side by side on a towel, looking out to the shimmering horizon of Liverpool Bay, with a transistor radio piping out a song by Tony Monopoly, when all at once a strange red cloud descended from the pure azure sky. The 'cloud' turned out to be a plague of ladybirds, and these tiny red and black beetles, which had over-multiplied as a result of the unprecedented heat wave, were dying of starvation after their normal food supply had become exhausted.

The ravenous ladybirds nibbled at anything upon which they happened to land, including the skin of Chris and Jan, and the two of them soon became covered in a thick Vermillion layer of the crawling, biting insects. Grabbing their belongings, the couple fled half blinded back to the sanctuary of their Vauxhall Chevette, and already the car was scarlet with a moving encrustation of the spotted bugs.

Once inside the vehicle, the couple began to wipe away the layer of insects. Chris spat them out of his mouth and Jan shook them from her hair as thousands more of the ladybirds rained down on the car with a sickening patter. Chris eventually drove off from the beachfront and took Jan to her mother's home in the Crossens district. That night, the couple went for a drink, and laughed about the way they had been caught up in the plague of ladybirds, even though it hadn't seemed funny to them at the time. Little did they suspect, that before the night was out, the ladybird affair would have paled into insignificance against the background of what they were about to experience.

By midnight, Chris and Jan were back at the same spot on the beach, close to the water's edge, exactly where they had been courting before the bug storm had hit. A full moon now hung overhead, its reflection shimmering far out to sea. The summer night air was warm, and the beach was totally deserted. The lapping tide was the only sound to be heard as the couple hugged and kissed. Each made vows of undying love to the other, as the night-tide rolled in, topped with moonlight-glistening foam – and a body!

Jan spotted it first, and pointed tremblingly to the incoming waters. Chris sat up in the sand and squinted at the dark but unmistakable form of a body with a pallid face. He jumped up and walked closer to the figure as Jan warned him to be careful – although she couldn't have said of what. Chris waded ankle-deep into the swirling foam mixed with seaweed scraps at the water's edge and surveyed the strangely-dressed woman, who was lying on her back in the wet sand with arms stretched out sideways, being pushed and pulled by the incoming waves like some great piece of flotsam. She looked old fashioned, dressed as she was in a white blouse buttoned up to the neck and a long ankle-length dress. A pair of dark boots protruded from under the hem of the soaked dress. The woman had dark, swept-back hair, and her face was deathly white.

Chris knelt by the side of the inert body and felt under the angle of her jaw for signs of a carotid pulse – but as he had suspected, there was none. He had had a few to drink that night and was struggling to recall the first-aid procedure for resuscitation, when suddenly, the eyelids of the washed-up woman fluttered for a few seconds, then opened to reveal a pair of large eyes with staring black irises. The woman smiled and water came trickling from her mouth, accompanied by an unsettling gurgling sound from deep within her body. A small crab-like creature scuttled out of the side of her mouth, and at the same time the woman grabbed Chris by his ankle with a strong ice-cold grip.

Jan let out a scream as she saw her boyfriend topple and fall into the shallow water, kicking wildly at the body to free himself. Somehow he did manage to break free and run back up the beach to his girlfriend.

The quaintly-attired woman lay there motionless once again with the tide rushing over her as the couple ran off into the night. Chris telephoned the police who were soon upon the scene. A group of them was soon sweeping their torches over the entire length of the beach, but they could find no trace of the washed-up woman. Chris feared that he'd be charged for wasting police time, but a sergeant reassured him that they had received similar reports about a woman being washed up countless times before around that time of year, and each time they found nothing, although, of course, they always had to investigate, just in case. It was always the same description too; the old fashioned clothes, the buttoned up blouse and the swept-back hair. However, this was the first time that anyone had reported that the woman had shown any sign of life, or made a grab at them.

Chris and Jan were naturally disturbed by their spine-chilling experience on the beach, and as they drove back to Liverpool later that morning, they went over and over the events of the previous night. The sergeant was right, of course. The very same sea-ghoul had been seen many times before over the years, washed up on the shores at Southport. I even have reports and newspaper clippings of the ghost which date back to Victorian times.

As to whose ghost it is, one elderly Southport resident is convinced that the apparition on the beach is the spirit of a passenger from an ill-fated ship that went down in Morecambe Bay in the nineteenth century.

~

An even more more animated seafront spectre was encountered in the early 1950s at Garston. In the middle of the witching hour of 1am, in November 1951, an elderly man named William Routledge was getting ready to dismantle the *Fides*, a German ship that dated back to the 1850s, at his ship-breaking yard, situated at the bottom of Brunswick Street. You will agree that he had chosen a rather strange time to begin the task, but so it was. He was walking slowly round the great rusting hulk of the *Fides,* trying to assess where and how best to start the salvage operation, when something strange happened which sent shivers up his spine.

Mr Routledge was accompanied that night by his wife and sister-in-law, and when the incident took place, it was Mrs Routledge's sister who first brought William's attention to the amorphous thing that was lingering in the shadows at the edge of the wasteland which adjoined the ship-breaking yard. Mr Routledge himself could make out nothing unusual, and assumed that if indeed there was anyone there, it would perhaps be a courting couple, as the area had long been a type of lover's lane on the banks of the Mersey. Meanwhile, the headlights of Mr Routledge's car threw harsh beams of light on the decrepit skeleton of the old German barque, starkly illuminating the barnacled hull and the three masts – an imposing if rather sad spectacle.

As William pondered about the best way to tackle the dismantling of the ship, his sister-in-law once again insisted with even more urgency that she could see something lurking in the nearby stretch of wasteland. Mr and Mrs Routledge looked over to the spot where she was pointing, and initially, all they could make out was the winking blue light of Speke Airport's beacon way off in the distance. Then, all of a sudden, an abnormally tall silhouette of a male figure loomed up out of the darkness. As they drew nearer, Mr Routledge and his sister-in-law could clearly see the stranger, who looked both sinister and slightly outrageous at the same time. He was over six-foot six in height, with a great shock of hair standing on end, and he walked with a pronounced stoop. What the observers simply could not comprehend, was the way the tall skinny man was seemingly able to walk in mid-air, for his feet were stepping on the gaps between the dykes.

The weird figure strode straight into the full glare of the car's headlamps – yet the beams cast no shadows from the gangly man – and with the extra illumination from the vehicle, it was possible to make out that he was wearing tapered, old-fashioned, plum-coloured breeches.

Now for a strange twist to this spooky tale.

William Routledge and his sister-in-law could plainly see the manifestation in all its detail, but Mrs Routledge, on the other hand, saw nothing whatsoever throughout the duration of the haunting and had no idea what they were talking about. She thought the pair of them had gone mad. This is a fairly common occurrence in the sphere of the supernatural, for some people are highly open and susceptible to psychic experiences and are able to see ghosts with great clarity, whereas others can see nothing, even when a ghost is being vividly witnessed by people in their company. The figure carried on walking straight through the beams of the car's headlights that November morning, before vanishing into thin air upon reaching the corrugated-iron fence which enclosed the yard.

Which, like so many hauntings, leaves us with the question of who was the ghost that walked in the ship-breaking yard early that November morning? No one knows to this day, but somewhere in the vast archives of Liverpool there must exist some painting, some photograph, or some etching of an eccentric

Victorian gentleman with that distinctive shock of vertical hair. Once we can identify the ghost, we may be able to discover why he returned to life on the Garston shore that morning. It is possible that his shade was brought forth by the impending dismantling of the Bremen barque *Fides*.

When consecrated ground is disturbed during excavation, or when an old building is altered or demolished, ghosts that have lain dormant for years often come back out of the woodwork, and I feel as if this might be the case with the odd-looking phantom which put in an appearance at the Garston ship-breaking yard. Perhaps the spectre was that of a former captain or shiphand of the *Fides*, coming back to take one last look at the old ship before departing on that final voyage to the world beyond.

The Arithmetic, however, except in the second standard was poor and unintelligent. Most of the children examined in this subject failed to pass the examination. Mental Arithmetic was practically a failure, so was the attempt to add up columns of pounds, shillings and pence. Pretty fair intelligence was on the whole, shown in English. The Needlework was very fair. Geography was only moderate. The Singing by Note was not good enough to merit the recommendation of the higher grant. More attention should be given to Reading and Numbers in the Infant Class." No grant is payable under Art. 105, as

THE EYE

On the Tuesday afternoon of 1 November 1887, a terrific gale from the Irish Sea struck Liverpool. All traffic on the Mersey was suspended in the treacherous weather, and inland, the whining, winnowing wind whipped fallen leaves against the rattling windows of the vicarage on Thomas Lane, Knotty Ash, as two stern-looking Homburg-hatted men in flapping black ankle-length coats approached. The Reverend Frank Powell was seated at his writing bureau, buried in thought, composing the first draft of a sermon for the following Sunday, when he noticed the visitors walking up the garden path, battling against the wind and holding on to their hats.

The bell jangled and the Reverend Powell opened the door to admit Superintendent Morgan O'Brien and Inspector John Johnston. Reverend Powell escorted the two men into his sitting room and invited them to take a seat by the fire, assuming that they had come to discuss one of his parishioners. He was deeply shocked when he learned why the two senior policemen had decided to pay him a visit. Apparently, a spate of malicious, accusatory letters, all written in green ink, had been received of late by several people in the upper echelons of Liverpool society. All of the letters were simply signed 'The Eye'.

Superintendent O'Brien explained that one of the recent letters of The Eye had been analysed using oblique illumination from an electric light, and the distinctive imprint of the name 'Frank Powell' had been revealed upon the sheet. There was a strong possibility that the impression had been made unintentionally as the author of the poison pen letter wrote his name on a leaf of paper lying across the page above the one that would be used to accuse various people of serious crimes and extra-marital affairs.

A sample of the Reverend's handwriting was compared to the calligraphy of The Eye, but there was no match and so the policemen apologised for interrupting the writing of his sermon and returned to the Central Police Office at 111 Dale Street. They were back to square one. Earlier that morning they had visited the Copperas Hill home of a man named Frank Napoleon Powell, but his handwriting bore no resemblance to the scathing green script of The Eye either. Another Frank Powell was visited at his home at Menai Street, Birkenhead, but this Mr Powell was a coachman who could barely write his name, never mind create sophisticated works of character assassination.

Some days later, at Number 27 Abercromby Square, Professor James Campbell Brown, DS, FCS, a prominent expert on chemistry at University College and a well-respected analyst for the County of Lancaster, received a scurrilous letter from The Eye, which threatened to destroy his career. The letter contained accusations of a highly shocking nature concerning his simultaneous relationships with two ladies and his abuse of narcotic drugs.

Superintendent O'Brien immediately analysed the letter for another accidental impression, but found none. Professor Campbell Brown was quick to accuse a John H Lightbody, a gentleman who lived on Sefton Drive, as the author of the letter, but when the detectives obtained a search warrant for the premises and analysed Lightbody's letters, it was obvious that his handwriting did not match that of The Eye's.

It was clear that whoever The Eye was, he was able to obtain an in-depth knowledge of the people he targeted with his spiteful letters. Superintendent O'Brien tried to find a common denominator which would link all of the victims, and therefore help to pinpoint the perpetrator. Had one man managed to move in all the different social circles of the distinguished people who received the letters? Lists of guests who had attended soirées and dinner parties at the homes of the rich victims were compiled and endlessly sifted through for clues, but all to no avail.

Immense pressure was put on Superintendent O'Brien to catch The Eye by Captain Nott Bower, the Head Constable of Lancashire who had a personal reason for wanting the man caught as quickly as possible. A prominent friend of his had been besmirched in one of the letters – and he was no less a person than the Lord Mayor!

The letter accusing the Lord Mayor of Liverpool of indulging in various 'unspeakable vices' also threatened that he would be killed in his bed when he least expected it. The letter and envelope were painstakingly analysed by Superintendent O'Brien, and the detective became animated when his magnifying glass picked up the faintest scrawl of a name written in pencil on the reverse of the page. That barely visible name was that of a Frederic Zerega. Could The Eye have accidentally used a page he had inadvertently written on previously, or was it a deliberate red herring? Superintendent O'Brien was not prepared to underestimate his quarry – he recognised that he was dealing with a very astute operator.

His detectives and constables scoured business directories, criminal records and electoral registers, and within the hour, the team discovered that a Frederic Zerega was a rich cotton merchant who conducted his business at the Albany buildings on Old Hall Street, just around the corner from the Central Police Office on Dale Street. Armed with a revolver, O'Brien, accompanied by plain-clothed police constables John Cain and Jim Law, proceeded to apartment 58 at the prestigious Albany buildings, where they were admitted by a junior clerk, who queried the business of the visitors. O'Brien explained who he was and after producing the necessary proof of his authority, he and his constables were ushered into the room where Frederic Zerega was reading through several telegrams. The illustrious cotton merchant was used to being treated with deference and respect and became enraged at the idea of being suspected of writing the poison pen letters. He warned Superintendent O'Brien that he would not hesitate to sue for damages if the search of his premises was protracted enough to disrupt his valuable business time.

O'Brien asked Zerega for a recent sample of his handwriting, and he soon saw to his dismay that the cotton merchant's calligraphy was a spidery illegible scrawl. O'Brien apologised and left the Albany in a huff. Once again the investigation had ground to a halt, just when it seemed that they were on to something. He had to conclude that The Eye was playing games with him, and that he had deliberately written Zerega's name on the back of the letter to mislead him. This was getting serious, his reputation was on the line and yet he felt he was going round in circles.

Then came a break in the baffling case which sent Superintendent Morgan O'Brien and his two burly constables at breakneck speed by hansom cab to Falkner Street. A boy had been on his way to post a letter at a pillar box when a dog being walked by a butcher whose surname was Peat had somehow slipped from its leash and attacked the youngster, inflicting a serious bite to his leg. The boy dropped the envelope he'd been about to post and ran off up the street in tears. Mr Peat picked up the letter at the foot of the pillar box and noticed something very strange about the address. The envelope read 'Archibald Bathgate, 235 & 237 Falkner Street'. Peat was puzzled because this address was less than a hundred yards away from the pillar box, so why hadn't the boy posted it through the letter box directly, rather than go through the trouble of posting it in a pillar box?

The butcher took the letter to Archibald Bathgate's house where he explained to him the events which had just taken place. Bathgate opened the envelope and unfolded the small foolscap page. At the top of the document was the weird drawing of a staring eye, and beneath it a very nasty letter claiming that he beat his wife regularly and had driven one of his maids to commit suicide after wrongly accusing her of theft. The last line of that green-inked letter stated: 'Your throat shall be cut from ear to ear.' With the butcher still there, Bathgate immediately called in the police. The Eye had struck again, only this time the police could connect the letter with the boy who had been bitten by the butcher's dog.

O'Brien asked the butcher if he had noticed where the boy had run to after being bitten, and Peat said that he was almost sure that he had run to Number 20 Falkner Street. Peat then apologised profusely for his dog Toby's behaviour, and said it was out of character for him to attack anyone, let alone a child. He would keep a much closer eye on him in the future.

The police superintendent and the two constables called at the address indicated by the butcher right away, and were admitted by the butler into the grand residence of a wealthy ship owner named David Ramsay. At his writing bureau, O'Brien found a pot of green ink, and upon the blotter, faint patches of a familiar reversed handwriting were evident. At long last they had found The Eye – or at least that's what Superintendent O'Brien assumed at first, but he was wrong. Not a single specimen of David Ramsay's handwriting matched that of The Eye's distinctive italicised script. Mrs Ramsay's handwriting was analysed, as well as the butler's, and even the maids and a junior servant gave samples of their penmanship, but none of their styles matched that of The Eye. Therefore, in a great huff, David Ramsay ordered the Superintendent and the policemen to leave his home immediately.

Superintendent O'Brien was very reluctant to leave because he strongly felt that the solution to the mystery of The Eye lay in that house. As he was following the butler across the hall, he suddenly had a wild thought. He stopped in his tracks, and asked the butler to summon the master of the house. Mr Ramsay reappeared from the drawing room with an agitated look about him, and before he could speak, Superintendent O'Brien asked if there was a boy staying at the house. After a lengthy pause, Mr Ramsay admitted that there was, and the detective asked if he could have a word with him.

"Whatever for?" Ramsay queried, indignantly.

"I would like to see his handwriting, sir," came the unexpected reply.

"How preposterous!" the ship owner exclaimed, but O'Brien firmly repeated his request with a steely gaze.

A child of nine years of age was then fetched down from the library of the house by the butler. He was David Ramsay's nephew, and his name was Percy Poole. O'Brien immediately noticed that the boy's left knee was bandaged. However, the child didn't appear to be in the least bit nervous or apprehensive, and his eyes had a wisdom that did not belong in a face so fresh and young. When he spoke it was with the voice of a man in his forties, and this out-of-place vocal maturity was very unnerving to the superintendent and the police constables.

"Let's get on with this then," he said, and his Uncle David took him to the bureau in the drawing room.

Percy was asked to write what the superintendent dictated in the green ink, and although he attempted to disguise his handwriting, he was not cunning enough to mask the tell-tale idiosyncrasies of his distinctive script. The way he indented paragraphs, and crossed his t's and dotted his i's made it obvious that, improbable though it seemed, this evil little genius was none other than The Eye. Of course, O'Brien knew that any case against the minor would be laughed out of court, but David Ramsay, anxious to avoid a scandal, personally assured the detective that his nephew would never write another poison pen letter. He also explained how the wunderkind's mother had died from a fever three years ago, and how his father was now dying from consumption.

Superintendent O'Brien had to settle for this outcome, although he would dearly have loved to wrap the whole affair up with a high profile trial. He was still curious to know how the boy had gained such intimate knowledge of the lives of the people he had written to. Mr Ramsay stepped in and explained that his nephew was a very good listener with a vast retentive memory, and had often been caught eavesdropping on the many conversations and tittle-tattle that had taken place at the soirées held regularly at the house. He had also listened to and absorbed the gossip of servants below stairs who had formerly worked at the households of many of The Eye's victims.

The misguided child's uncle was as good as his word and the boy who had terrorised the upper classes of Liverpolitan society was never again allowed to take up his poisoned pen, and The Eye ceased his postal persecutions of the immoral élite.

THE SHARED DREAM

In the 1970s in a certain area of Liverpool, a bully who can only be described as evil, was making the lives of a group of thirteen-year-old children a living hell. This was in an era when Child Line was undreamt of; when many uneducated parents would say to their bullied sons and daughters: "Give them a belt back, or they'll walk all over you."

But no one in their right mind would have considered hitting back at the bully who preyed on the younger pupils of a certain senior school in north Liverpool. We shall call the bully Mike.

At the age of fourteen Mike had already surpassed six feet in height, and now, at sixteen, in the final year of secondary school, he was filling out dramatically, probably on the chocolate bars and sweets he was forever seizing from his unfortunate victims. Like all bullies, Mike had surrounded himself with a group of sidekicks and fawning cronies, and even these pseudo-loyal followers came in for a severe beating now and then. Mike's father was an appalling role model, having been in and out of prison, on a regular basis, for most of his adult life, and his petite mum was completely cowed by her aggressive son.

What is more, things were getting worse of late. In a fit of temper, Mike had given his mother a black eye one day and wrung the neck of her budgerigar, simply because she had bought him the wrong brand of bottle-green flares. The police were brought in by Mike's fuming uncle but the bully's mother refused to testify against her son through a mixture of fear and love and claimed that the whole thing had been an accident; she had walked into a door. Mike and his gang wrecked his uncle's Cortina that night and sprayed 'GRASS' across the doors in silver paint.

One afternoon, in the school playground, Mike grabbed a timid, bespectacled thirteen-year-old boy named Philip by his ear and dragged him to the toilets where he snatched hold of his hair and started twisting it painfully. During this abduction, the cigar-chewing maths teacher on playground duty had been craftily distracted by two of Mike's lackeys, who had asked him to explain the difference between net and gross earnings. Meanwhile, in the toilets, Mike's right-hand man, Batesy, kept watch at the door, while Philip found himself shoved into a cubicle.

"Do you want to buy some looseys?" Mike asked, and produced a packet of Player's No. 6 cigarettes.

"I ... I ... d d don't smoke," stammered Philip, trying to keep the tremor out of his voice.

"Well then, you're just about to start, okay, my little friend?"

Mike slid a cigarette out of the box and lit it with a golden Ronson lighter. He took a long drag on the filter tip and exhaled straight into Philip's face. Then he said, "Open your mush," and the boy opened his mouth without hesitation. He had seen too many heads cracked by Mike to even consider putting up any resistance. Mike thrust the cigarette into the boy's quivering mouth and ordered him to smoke it.

"Okay, Mike," Philip said, with the twitching cigarette apparently stuck to his lip. He puffed out smoke, and some of the exhalation accidentally went into Mike's eyes.

The bully let out a string of shocking pornographic-sounding expletives then shouted, "Smoke it properly you stupid four-eyes! Breathe it in you jessy!"

Philip had always had a weak chest and was probably asthmatic, and he started to cough and splutter, unable to catch his breath. In the panic of breathlessness he made the mistake of trying to push past Mike – and swiftly received a hard slap which knocked his spectacles down the toilet pan and made him see flashes of light, even though his eyes were closed tight.

The boy then stumbled and hit his ribs on the hard toilet seat, badly bruising his side. He looked up at the blurred image of the bully, then felt a sharp kick in the crotch which badly winded him and caused him to throw up all over the bully's shoes, and of course, this sent Mike into a frenzy. He tore a roll towel off its spindle with the intention of strangling Philip with it, but in the nick of time, the maths teacher arrived upon the scene after a tip-off from a young pupil who had heard the attack in the toilet.

"Get your hands off me, or I'll have you done in!" Mike bawled at the teacher as he seized his arm.

"Will you now, sonny?" smiled the teacher, who was a Fifth Dan Black Belt in Karate who was able to restrain Mike effortlessly. "You know something, I can't wait until you're expelled, lad," he said. "We don't want the likes of you

With that, he marched with him out of the toilets, where he instructed a caretaker to go and see if the kid in the cubicle was alright.

The headmaster visited Mike's mother at home and warned her once again about her son's totally unacceptable behaviour, and once again she told him how she herself had considered leaving home to get away from his violent ways. It was a no-win situation, no matter which way you looked at it.

The following Monday morning at 10.30pm, a thirteen-year-old boy was rushed from the playground into the medical room, bleeding profusely from his nose. This time Mike's gang had surrounded the boy in a scrum as the naive new English teacher had looked on, sipping a cup of tea as he patrolled the playground. "Boys will be boys," he thought. He was brought up with a start as the pupils began to disperse to reveal a child lying prostrate and inert on the cold macadam. That boy was Nick. It was he who had told the maths teacher about the beating his friend Philip was receiving from Mike on the Friday afternoon. Nick paid with a broken nose, and when he returned to school on the following day with a dressing on his face, he was too afraid to identify the culprits in the line-up. The headmaster unknowingly made things much worse by caning the three smirking members of Mike's gang anyway.

That day the torn-out page of an exercise book was placed in Philip's desk by someone while he was out in the playground. Upon that piece of paper, someone who couldn't spell had scrawled a chilling threat in block letters. It read: 'YOU WIL BE FOUND WHITH A NIFE IN YOUR BACK,' and this warning was accompanied by a drawing of a dagger dripping with blood.

When the bell rang an hour later, signifying the end of school for the day, Nick was getting ready to leave the classroom when he noticed that someone had slashed his blazer with a knife. He and Philip walked down the school corridor in trepidation, dreading the dark area beyond the self-closing doors that led to the gymnasium. Mike and his gang usually lurked there just by the exit, waiting to collar their victims. The two frightened boys loitered about in the corridor, hoping that the English teacher would accompany them, but instead he came out of the classroom whistling, seemingly oblivious to the boys' plight and went upstairs to chat to the female art teacher he was becoming quite fond of.

Nick and Philip decided to risk going out of the school by the exit on the other side of the building, but this proved to be a big mistake because Mike was waiting there with his deputy Batesy. The bully grabbed Nick by his tie.

"Oh look, Batesy!" he sneered. "It's little Nicholas ridiculous with the broken nose."

Batesy laughed, looked around, then grabbed Philip by the arm. He head-butted the boy, and watched as he sank to his knees, crying.

Nick was horrified. Then Mike told him what he could expect tomorrow.

"You know that acid tank in the metalwork room?"

Nick was too terrified even to nod.

"Well, your hand's going in there tomorrow," Mike promised with glee.

"Stop crying, you little Mary Ellen," said Batesy, looking down at the sobbing Philip.

The geography teacher heard the commotion and coming out of his classroom shouted, "Hey! What's going on?" from the far end of the corridor, but Mike and Batesy slipped away before he could reach them. The teacher asked Philip what the matter was, and the boy took his spectacles off and wiped away the tears.

"Nothing sir."

"Who were those two boys who were here just now?" he asked, but Nick just shrugged and Philip said nothing, both fearing further reprisals if they gave the names of the bullies to the teachers.

On their way home from school, the boys decided that they needed to take a long walk in order to decide what to do. Nick said that they couldn't stay at the school any longer and suggested running away from home. He reminded Philip how, just a few weeks ago, Mike had been forced to abandon his attempt to dip another young pupil's hand in the tank of sulphuric acid in the metalwork room after the headmaster walked in unexpectedly. The boy had been held in a head-lock by Batesy, as Mike had been forcing the terrified boy's hand down towards the highly corrosive liquid. Days later, Mike's macabre fixation with the acid bath was satisfied when he snatched a first year boy's white pet mouse and lowered it into the tank by its tail. They both agreed that they were dealing with a madman who would stop at nothing once he'd got his teeth into you.

Philip then showed his friend the threatening note he had found in his desk, and that finally convinced Nick that the only way out was to run away from home. At that point something inside of Philip seemed to snap. He was blinking rapidly and looking into space with an expression of dread and didn't seem to know where he was.

"Phil!" shrieked Nick, grabbing the hood of his friend's parka and yanking him backwards, out of the path of a speeding car which narrowly missed him.

Philip seemed to be in a trance. He didn't even thank Nick for saving his life. Instead he said something very disturbing indeed.

"Nick, I'm going to murder Mike."

"You what?"

Nick was totally taken aback by this declaration. Philip was a gentle lad, he couldn't hurt a fly.

"My grandfather owns a gun, and I know where he keeps it," said Philip flatly.

He turned to his friend, and his eyes looked strange and empty, as if he was having a some kind of breakdown.

"Phil, don't talk like that," said Nick.

He shuddered because his friend certainly looked as if he had every intention of carrying out the threat. He said the words so coldly. It made Nick's flesh creep; this situation was getting way out of hand.

A lollipop man was walking down the pavement towards them and told the boys to cross with him further down the road.

"Don't even think of trying to stop me, Nick, because I'm in the mood to do something really bad, and if you stop me I'll kill myself, because I've had enough."

"Don't talk daft ... you can't ..." Nick glanced at the lollipop man, then whispered, "... go round shooting people, this isn't some stupid computer game. Stop it, Phil, you're scaring me."

That evening, Philip took Nick to his grandfather's flat, and as soon as the old man went out to the kitchen to make them a cup of tea, he sneaked into his room and came back holding an old Army service revolver. He briefly showed it to a horrified Nick, then stashed it in his satchel.

Later that night, Philip sat in Nick's bedroom, opening the chamber of the gun, just as he had seen his grandfather do so many times. It was loaded with five bullets. Nick pleaded with his friend not to go ahead with the planned murder, but Philip reminded him about the acid tank and the knife threat.

"You'll go to prison," Nick said, watching Philip roll the chambers.

"Only if they catch me, and they won't."

"The police aren't stupid, Phil. They will narrow it down to you and then there's your grandfather; he's going to know it's you when he sees the gun's been fired."

"They'll understand when I tell him how I was bullied," said Phil, and a lone tear, magnified by the lens of his spectacles, welled up and slid down his cheek.

"'Course they won't understand," said Nick, trying his utmost to dissuade his friend from committing the ultimate crime, "and you'll be a murderer."

Phil leaned forward and held his face in his right hand. His whole body was wracked with sobs, and the gun dangled limply from the other hand. Nick slowly reached out and took the weapon, and Philip put up no resistance whatsoever. He released the revolver, and Nick took it out of the room. He climbed the stairs and went up to the attic, where most of the junk of the house was chaotically stored. He removed a stack of documents from a biscuit tin and put the gun in there. He replaced the lid and then went back down to his friend, who had stopped crying and was now flipping through the pages of *Look-In* magazine.

"Let's go down and get something to eat," Nick said, and the two boys went down to the kitchen. Nick's mother had made a curry and the boys sat down and enjoyed their meals. Nick asked his mother if Phil could stay over, and she said he couldn't because it was a school night, but later relented. That night the boys slept top-tail in the bed, but they didn't fall asleep until almost 3am, because they were so worried about meeting Mike and Batesy in the morning.

Something very strange took place that morning at Nick's house. The boys experienced what is known as a 'shared dream', when two or more people have the very same dream. Some paranormal researchers who have catalogued such instances have hypothesised that the dream is shared telepathically by the dreaming minds. Whatever the true cause, Philip and Nick awoke at 8 o'clock that morning to a ringing alarm clock suffused with a peaceful feeling, which they couldn't explain, given the serious bullying problems they were both having to contend with. Neither of them could work out why, but they felt no fear or apprehension about going to school.

At the breakfast table, Nick said, "I had a weird dream last night about that Mike."

"So did I," said Philip, through a mouthful of toast.

"I dreamt he was lying in this bed and a woman was saying 'Get up!' and he wouldn't get up," said Nick.

Philip's jaw dropped, for the exact same thing had happened in his dream. Nick found this hard to believe, until Philip went on to tell him how the dream ended.

"The woman started screaming really loudly, and that really scared me. She looked insane, and she started to shake Mike, and then the room went all black."

Nick turned to his bemused mother, who had little knowledge of the traumatic trials her son was going through at the hands of Mike and his cohorts. She had believed her son when he had told her that his broken nose was the result of some rough and tumble in the playground.

79

"Both of you can't have had the same dream," she laughed, drawing on her mundane common sense.

"But that's just it, we did," Nick said, and he and Philip looked at one another with baffled expressions.

In the school assembly hall, Nick and Philip and a majority of the pupils noticed that Mike was absent and the communal sense of relief was almost tangible. The staff on the stage seemed to be in a very solemn mood for some reason and then the headmaster walked in and stood at the front row, gravely surveying the assembled school. He asked everyone to be quiet in an unusually soft voice, then asked the pupils to sit down. Choosing his words very carefully, he then told everyone the tragic news about the death of one of the school's pupils. Apparently, Mike had been found dead in his bed early that morning. The cause of death wasn't known, but later on, in the local newspapers, that rather vague term 'natural causes' was mentioned. The article also described how Mike's mother – unable to accept his sudden death – had tried desperately to shake her son awake on his deathbed before her hysterical screams brought her neighbours running to the house.

Nick and Philip felt cold shivers when they read the newspaper piece, and instantly recalled the weird dream they had both shared. Nick admitted that on the night when they had shared that dream, just before he fell asleep, he had prayed to God, asking him to somehow stop the bullies at the school. Was the resulting shared dream and the sudden death of Mike some strange coincidence, or were Nick's prayers somehow answered?

Batesy lost no time in trying to take over from Mike, but was expelled from the school after he was caught red-handed holding a pupil's head down a toilet. The culture of bullying soon ended after Batesy's departure. Nick and Philip began to look forward to attending school after that dark period, and both lads ended up going to university.

STRANGE CHARACTERS KNOCKING ABOUT

Sneaking into my childhood home one night, long after I was supposed to have been safely tucked up in bed, my mother collared me in the hallway with the stealth and swiftness of a Ninja, and after interrogating me about my whereabouts for the past few hours, she warned me to come home as soon as she called me in future because, she said, rather enigmatically: "There are some very strange characters knocking about this time of night."

That sentence captured my young imagination, and I immediately visualised a motley assortment of weird-looking figures prowling about the twilit neighbourhood on a nightly basis. However, my mother's warning was not without foundation, I later discovered.

In the late summer of 1972, a number of women had been followed by an odd-looking couple who had been seen loitering about in the area where I lived. On one occasion they had followed a young woman from her workplace on Mount Pleasant, all the way to a tenement called Myrtle House, where the couple (who were dressed in drab old-fashioned clothes that seemed to date from the 1950s) waited in the middle of a square, gazing up at the woman's flat. The woman's boyfriend ran down into the square to confront the couple, who looked as if they were in their thirties, but by the time the young man has descended the six flights of stairs, the peculiar duo had vanished without a trace.

Later that evening, a man and a woman, described as wearing the same type of outdated clothes as the stalkers seen at Myrtle House, were seen in Toxteth, where they tried to entice a twelve-year-old boy into a car on Upper Hampton Street. The boy, surnamed Clarke, described the woman's eyes as large and staring, and he said that she talked in a voice that sounded tinny like the voice of his sister's doll when she pulled the cord on its back. The police naturally viewed this piece of bizarre information with some amusement and did not take it seriously.

A little under a week later, the odd couple turned up in Speke, and this time they were getting around in a vehicle that was as antiquated as them; a bottle-green 1960s Ford Anglia 307E van. They approached children waiting to be served at a mobile shop, but a wary adult who saw the couple talking to the children alerted a policeman, who rushed to the scene just in time to see the van speed off. The vehicle was later seen on Horrocks Avenue, but soon vanished into the summer twilight, and the strangely attired couple were not seen again.

There is something about the descriptions of the out-of-date couple that reminds me of the so-called 'Men in Black' – those mysterious but well-documented figures that have been known to harass witnesses who have encountered UFOs. They not only wear black clothes but their attire is usually decades behind the times, yet the vintage cars they have been known to drive paradoxically always look and smell brand new. The term Men in Black is something of a misnomer though, as encounters with Women in Black have also been reported over the years.

In 1966, a woman I shall call Judith returned to her home on Childwall Valley Road one afternoon after a shopping trip, and found a strange-looking couple right outside the windows of her lounge, trying to look in. Judith hurried up the path to the front door, and said, "Hello, can I help you?"

A very peculiar-looking man and a woman turned around to face her with a series of jerky movements, as if they were marionettes. The man's hair looked like a bad wig and his face seemed to be coated with thick, pancake make-up. He wore a dark cardigan and black narrow trousers and ankle-length boots. The woman's hair also looked synthetic and her face was also plastered with make-up. She wore a dark coloured shirt, a black pullover and a knee-length dark purple skirt. The man spoke in a voice devoid of any accent, and said he was a friend of Judith's husband. Judith thought the name he gave sounded like 'Mariocki' – and she had never heard her husband mention that surname before. Her husband was a rep with a firm that specialised in catering equipment, and he was currently down in Derbyshire on business. He was not expected back home for a few days, but as Mr Mariocki said he'd travelled up from London with his wife to see his "old friend" Judith invited them into the house for a while.

It soon became patently clear that Mariocki did not know her husband at all. Judith had asked him how he had come to know him and the strange-looking man had said that he had been in the Army with him, but Judith knew that this was nonsense because her husband had been in the Navy. When Judith asked the Maricokis if they preferred tea or coffee, they looked at one another awkwardly as if they were stuck for an answer, the woman eventually saying, "No thanks".

Fifteen tense minutes elapsed as the odd couple sat side by side on a two-seater sofa, struggling to make conversation. The man finally stood up and asked if he could have a look round the garden, but Judith, feeling very uneasy about the behaviour of the visitors, made an excuse to encourage them to leave. She told them that she had to go to her mother's home, and even put on her coat, but the couple just stood there bewildered, seemingly unable to take the hint.

Judith decided to go next door and tell her neighbour, a pensioner named Stan, about the weird people she'd foolishly let into her home, perhaps he would help her to get rid of them. Stan accompanied Judith into her house to confront the strangers, but the couple had gone. Stan and Judith checked all the rooms of the house and even the garden, but there was no sign of them. Judith was relieved, but the sudden disappearance left her feeling decidedly edgy. What did they want? What if they were to return? Stan promised to keep a close eye out of them and she should call him at any hour if anything untoward happened.

At around half-past two in the morning, the telephone rang on Judith's bedside table, and when she answered the call, she heard a chattering noise which sounded like a woodpecker pecking at a tree – then the line went dead. Judith tried to settle back down in her bed, telling herself that the call had just been some telephonic fault, when she heard a sound which seemed to come from the back of the house – in the garden. She put on her nightgown and slippers, then left the bedroom. She tiptoed across the landing to the toilet, where she gingerly opened the window. She looked down into the garden, and there was the couple who had visited her earlier in the day, prowling about near the back hedge. Judith called the police, but when they arrived at the house the Maricokis had gone.

Judith's husband turned up a day later and when she told him all about the peculiar couple he confirmed her suspicions; he knew no one by the name of Mariocki, in fact he thought they had probably made the name up.

About a week later, the couple were spotted on Abbeystead Road by Judith and her mother as they returned from a trip to the Abbey Cinema in Wavertree. The two strange-looking people followed them as far as the Fiveways Roundabout, where a policeman was chatting to a youth. Upon seeing the police constable, Mr and Mrs Mariocki did a swift U-turn and walked back the way they had come, never to be seen again.

Judith also had the strong sensation that there was something strange about the whole area where she lived during that period in the 1960s. Just a few years before, in December 1962, a twelve-year-old schoolgirl named Lesley Hobbs had been brutally murdered at Number 191 Childwall Valley Road, the last house on the left before the railway bridge. The murder had taken place on a Sunday night, as the moon was full, and in the newspaper there was talk of a 'Full Moon Murderer' who killed by the lunar phases. This unusual line of thinking came about when detectives who worked on the Hobbs murder wondered if the killing of Maureen Ann Dutton on nearby Thingwall Lane in the previous December – around the time of the winter solstice (21 December) had been carried out by the same person. The moon was full around that date, but the detectives later played down the suggestion of a Moon-obsessed ritual killer.

At around 11.30pm on the night of the Childwall Valley Road killing, Ronald and Maureen Hobbs, the parents of the murdered girl, returned home and found Lesley brutally murdered with her hands tied behind her back. She had been stabbed and battered over the head with a poker and a metal ashtray stand. The couple had gone out earlier in the evening at about 9.30pm, leaving Lesley to look after the younger family members: John, aged nine, Janet, aged seven, and Patricia, aged five. All of these younger children had remained sound asleep in the upstairs bedroom and had not been disturbed by the killer. The girl had been listening to pop songs on the radio at the time of the murder, and must have admitted the killer (or killers) into the house, as there was no sign of a forced entry.

A neighbour of the Hobbs family stated: "We heard bangs at about ten fifteen to ten thirty, but as we were in bed, we did not pay any particular attention because we thought the children were having fun."

The murder investigation soon got into full swing, and senior police officers received numerous reports of two men who had been seen in the vicinity of the murder scene. The men were sighted at the time when Mr and Mrs Hobbs had left their home on Childwall Valley Road by friends of the family and other passers-by. Bert Balmer, the Chief Constable of Liverpool, and Detective Chief Superintendent James Morris, Head of the CID, gave the *Liverpool Echo* the descriptions of the two men: "Youngish, medium height and build, fair hair, wearing a donkey jacket-styled coat and jeans. The second man was a little shorter in height, dark, and wearing a dark overcoat."

These two men were later seen running away from the murder scene. The suspects were never found, despite a massive door-to-door police inquiry and a widespread search of the neighbourhoods surrounding Childwall.

As with numerous cases where the disreputable Balmer was involved, the Childwall Valley Road murder took a bizarre turn when police failed to arrest the two men who had been seen running away. Instead, a fifteen-year-old office boy named Peter William Rix, was arrested and charged with the murder. Rix was alleged to have told his mother after he was taken to the police station that he had killed Lesley. Rix pleaded not guilty to the murder, but was found guilty of manslaughter and was detained for life. According to a Dr Benedict Finkelman, the superintendent of Rainhill Mental Hospital, Rix had a deep dislike of girls, and it had led him to kill Lesley. The only forensic evidence linking Rix to the murder was the discovery of a spot of blood – Group B, Lesley's group – was found on Rix's overcoat by Inspector Joseph Townsend. Rix said it was probably from a cut he'd suffered after sliding down an embankment, but Rix's blood group was O. Then Detective Chief Inspector Ernest Richardson conducted a search of Rix's home and announced that behind a wardrobe in an upstairs room he had found a knife, with which, it was alleged, the girl had been stabbed.

Who were the two adults seen in the vicinity of the murder scene at 9.30 and 10.25pm that night? Balmer gave up looking for them as soon as the investigation had centred on Rix. Some wondered if two people had killed Lesley, as she had been both battered and stabbed. Killers rarely bludgeon a person then start to stab them; they usually use a single weapon to kill, and I can't think of a single case of a killer who switched to another type of weapon in the frenzied heat of a murderous attack.

~

One of the strangest characters knocking around at night in the North West area has to be the woman who was encountered by a reader named Ian.

In the 1980s, when Ian was in his twenties, he and a friend sometimes frequented the Norseman Club near Liverpool Docks. One evening, Ian and his friends were at this club, when they got talking with a group of Peruvian sailors who had recently docked at the port. The seamen loved the company of the Liverpool lads with their distinctive accent and quirky sense of humour. As closing time at the Norseman loomed, the Peruvians invited Ian and his friends back to the ship to continue drinking and singing and possibly engaging in a game of poker.

The Liverpool lads followed the sailors to a dock where the security men allowed them on to the ship with the Peruvians, and Ian described how they had such a good time, that they didn't want to leave. However, as the night wore on, Ian's mates gradually left the ship one by one, and at around four in the morning, Ian decided that he'd better start making tracks home himself. He walked down the gangplank, into a bitterly cold winter's morning, and then started making his way towards the dock entrance, but saw it was closed with

85

several security men in attendance, so he decided instead to walk through an immense yard where several large portakabin-sized containers were stacked. One side of the fence surrounding this storage area ran parallel with the dock road, and Ian had every intention of climbing the fence at some point when he was out of view of the security guards.

A strange incident took place next and I will let Ian explain in his own words:

"I suddenly noticed a woman walking towards me. Now whether it was youthful stupidity, Dutch courage, or simple curiosity, I don't know, but I remember just standing there, watching this weird figure as she came towards me. She wore a short skirt and high heels, some type of short jacket, and she had a short hairstyle. But as she came closer it was her face and movement that struck me as weird. She didn't look at me, and didn't change her expression at all. She just walked like a robot with a fixed expression, and a wide-eyed look of fear, and she never once blinked or moved her eyes to look at me or anything else. Let's face it; meeting anyone at four in the morning at such a lonely place, you'd expect some reaction or conversation.

"As she walked in this undeviating direction towards me, whilst keeping this strange wide-eyed fixed stare, it got weirder, because as she came closer, I stepped aside to give her enough room to keep walking past me, but she did the strangest thing. Without even the slightest sideways glance, or giving any change of expression, or turning her head, she threw out her left arm to grab my arm whilst walking at her steady pace. My instinctive reaction was to pull my arm quickly from her grasp, which was more of a polite hold rather than an aggressive grab, and as I pulled away, I stepped back several paces. I remember being shocked at her sudden grab, and I remember shouting several questions at her about the reasons for her behaviour, and basically what she playing at, but I was questioning someone who was walking away, and so only had the view of her back as she walked on. But as she walked on in her intently purposeful way, I stood there alone in the dark eerie silence amongst the containers, and was suddenly overcome with fear. It's hard to explain, but it was like an unusual sense that something wasn't quite right.

"Anyway, I just knew that she wasn't normal, and I was so overcome with fear I somehow scaled the metal fence in no time, then jumped straight from the top of the fence on to the road below, and hit the ground running. I didn't look back or stop running until I was some distance away and felt safe."

The identity of this woman, if that is indeed what she was, remains a riddle.

There was no other way into that area where the containers were, only the way through which Ian had come, and he found it hard to imagine any prostitute standing there in the darkness on a freezing cold morning on the waterfront, in that god-forsaken place waiting for a client. Her strange fixed expression and lack of any reaction to Ian's presence – apart from the way she made a grab at him – is puzzling, and to this day, Ian believes there was something supernatural about that woman.

So remember, the next time you stay out late, keep your wits about you, because there are definitely some very strange characters knocking about!

MIDNIGHT WISH

Rain, descending in fitful showers, was sweeping against the window panes of the sandstone cottage at Olive Mount, Wavertree, in the Liverpool of 1951. Inside the cottage a bakelite radio blared out the *Adventures of P.C. 49* with Liverpool's own Brian Reece in the starring role. Twelve-year-old Danny Foster was perched on the edge of a fireside armchair, gazing into the glowing coal embers, lost in precious memories of the time when his mother was still alive. She had died from some terrible disease that his dad and gran refused to even talk about; all that Danny knew was that it had been in her bandaged bosom. Danny's father reclined in another easy chair smoking his pipe, gazing at the floor as the radio formed a series of pictures in his mind. Gran was in the kitchen washing clothes in the dolly tub, humming a sad old tune called *The Butcher Boy*.

The downpour thinned to a mizzle, and Danny cupped his hands to the rain speckled windowpanes and looked out into the gathering gloom. How he pined for a friend of his own age to play with. He and his father had moved from Anfield to live with his grandmother after his mother had died, and two months after starting at the new school, Danny still hadn't found a friend in the neighbourhood. For some reason he suddenly recalled a library book about superstitions and ghosts that he'd read. In the book it claimed that if a person made a wish at midnight, it was more likely to come true. It is difficult to imagine one of today's streetwise twelve-year-olds believing in such things as midnight wishes, but Danny was a typical child of the fifties and still retained that kind of innocence.

Well, midnight found Danny standing in the hall in his pyjamas and bare feet, avidly watching the face of the chiming grandfather clock. As the clock struck twelve, he closed his eyes and fervently wished for a new friend, and after the twelfth chime had faded into the stillness he trotted back off to bed. That night he had a strange dream about the local wood in Bowring Park, close to the golf course. The silhouette of a boy was beckoning to him, calling out his name. Danny felt an instant empathy with the boy and sensed that he was just as lonely as himself. The same dream was repeated in Danny's mind on the following night, and in the morning he set off for Bowring Park, convinced that the boy would be there.

Danny returned to the cottage that day a changed boy. He packed his little suitcase, and was about to leave when his grandmother cornered him.

"And where do you think you're going, Danny? And what's all this?" Mrs Foster asked, seizing the packing case.

Danny announced that he was going to live with his friend, but then flatly refused to say who this friend was, or where he lived. His gran grounded him until his father returned home from work. Danny's dad grilled him until the lad finally admitted that his friend lived "somewhere in the wood" at Bowring Park.

I've never seen any houses in that wood," remarked his father, dubiously. "Anyway, lad, all that's beside the point, you're not going anywhere. Your place is right here with me and your gran."

Danny response to this was very strange indeed, and was spoken as if he was quoting something he had heard: "Often do we look, seldom do we see. Often do we hear, seldom do we listen."

"Where did you get that from? You never thought of that yourself," said the father condescendingly.

That evening Danny broke down and cried and talked incoherently about his new friend, and complained, rather mysteriously, that if he didn't go to the wood his friend would leave without him, and that he'd never see him again.

"He's lonely as well, Gran, and he came to me because I wished for him, reached out for him you see."

Danny's words were punctuated with great gulping sobs. His grandmother felt his forehead, thinking he was ill, but he didn't have a temperature, or a furred tongue, or any of the other signs she used to look out for.

Then Danny's father saw it. Then his gran did, and then Danny himself. Something was looking at them through the cottage window in the twilight. It was oval-headed with huge eyes like a cat and a stick-like body.

"Jesus, Mary and Joseph!" said Mr Foster, his mind attempting to make sense of the unfamiliar being beyond the windows. His mother squinted through the window panes in puzzlement at first, then recoiled in horror. But Danny smiled and reached out towards the entity – his friend – but was restrained by his father. The small figure stood there for a minute, then raised its hand, as if to wave. After a few moments, it silently moved off and merged back into the darkness.

From that moment until the break of dawn, Danny was choked with an inexplicable, heart-rending sorrow. It felt like the type of pain that burned your heart when a best friend at school was forced to move to some far-flung parts because his father had found work in another county. This friend, Danny somehow sensed, had gone away to a far distant place where our fiery-mantled sun is seen as a dim star. The boy had no notion of light-years and parsecs, yet he felt the never-ending emptiness of unimaginable expanses of space swallowing up his friend.

Today, Danny has vague memories of the entity he met in Bowring Park wood, and firmly believes that the thing was an alien child that somehow answered his desperate longing for a friend that night in 1951. Had Danny gone to stay with his friend, one wonders where in the cosmos he would be by now.

Over the years, Danny has had occasional distinctive dreams in which he sees the face of the Bowring Park entity, and these dreams are always happy ones that leave him with a strong sense of well-being when he wakes up. Perhaps his interstellar friend manifests himself in the dreams through some form of telepathic communication which circumvents the earthly laws of Relativity. Danny doesn't talk about all this much, fearing the ridicule of his peers, but I remind him that this planet is surrounded on all sides by the infinite uncharted blackness of space, and that there are more stars, planets and galaxies out there than there are grains of sands on all the beaches of the world. We know about as much of this great Universe as an unborn baby knows about the ways of the world.

ECHOES FROM THE PAST

On the evening of Wednesday, 22 February 2006, at around 9pm, Gemma and Callum, two fifteen-year-olds, were walking up Score Lane in Childwall when they heard a bloodcurdling female scream. The teenagers stopped in their tracks and looked all around but could see no one in distress. Callum had been escorting his girlfriend home, so they walked on, but upon reaching the junction at Rocky Lane, another sound was heard which sounded like a large crowd brawling somewhere in the distance. In the midst of this inexplicable riot of sound, the same female scream pierced the cold evening air – then the unearthly screams abruptly ended.

Callum saw his girlfriend safely home, and as he returned to his own home he passed Rudston Junior and Infants school, where the teenager heard the same baffling sounds of uproar and commotion, punctuated by the same spine-chilling scream he'd heard earlier with Gemma. This time, an elderly man walking his dog up Okehampton Road heard the sound as well. The two stopped to compare notes and looked everywhere to see if there was anything amiss, but they could find nothing.

I have several reports on file of strange sounds in the Score Lane area, including an account of cannons being fired one evening in 1976. My own theory is that the sounds are the ghostly re-enactments of a past battle at the site. The field that runs alongside All Saints Church in Childwall has a very sinister reputation, and Score Lane runs through part of the site. For centuries this area has been known as 'Bloody Acre' and it seems that whatever happened there, involved the loss of a lot of lives. Local historians originally thought the name Bloody Acre might be a reference to a Civil War battle, or perhaps a skirmish from the days of the Reformation, but it is beginning to look as if something much more sinister went on in the area of Score Lane in times past, and perhaps it still echoes down the centuries to the present day. In fact, some think that some major pagan ritual involving human sacrifice took place on Bloody Acre.

～

Now for one of the most distressing stories I have covered in a long time. It is well known in the world of the paranormal that people who have suffered a nervous breakdown can sometimes attain a level of consciousness that makes them particularly receptive to extrasensory data in the form of precognition, and sometimes 'retrocognition' – a psychic way of seeing events of the past.

A young Bootle woman named Emily suffered a severe nervous breakdown at Christmas 2005, and she was hospitalised for almost a month as a result. Early in February, 2006, Emily went to spend a few weeks recuperating with a cousin in Fairfield, Kensington. On Saturday 11 February, Emily seemed cheerful and almost back to her normal self as she visited the Albert Dock. Afterwards she visited the Church of St Nicholas – and became hysterical. She described horrific visions of dead children, which convinced her cousin that she had become mentally unstable again. Emily was physically sick as she ran from the churchyard and was almost knocked down by a car on the dock road. She was so affected by her 'vision' that she had to be sedated with tranquillisers.

Emily later told me about the awful things that she had seen whilst she was in that church: "Dozens of children, all girls, were lying about on the lawn, disfigured, blood-soaked and flat, as if a steamroller had run over them," she said, still visibly upset by the memory of the awfulness of what she had witnessed.

Then Emily described how she was forced to watch as crowds of small-looking people in old fashioned clothes appeared, and they were all wailing and grieving pitifully around the bodies of the dead children. I listened sympathetically and took her description of this seeming massacre of the innocents seriously.

I later decided to research the history of the Church of St Nicholas, to see if this would throw up any clue as to the origin of Emily's vision. What I uncovered made me shudder with horror. Emily had experienced her vision on 11 February, and on that day in 1810, twenty-eight little girls were taking their seats in the Church of St Nicholas when the keystone to one of the arches of the building inexplicably became dislodged and crashed to the floor. The spire crumbled and collapsed within seconds and tons of masonry crashed down upon the girls, killing twenty-three of them instantly. A few who survived the initial impact of the collapse were brought out and laid on the grass but later died of their injuries, and some of their bodies were so crushed and flattened that they were almost beyond recognition.

I believe that Emily, in her highly receptive state of mind, somehow tuned into this tragic incident from one hundred and ninety-six years ago, and had the misfortune of experiencing the disaster almost at first hand.

SHIP IN A BOTTLE

Coincidences fascinate me. Are they merely the work of chance or are more sinister forces at work? For example, take the case of the three John Lennons. Ex-Beatle John Lennon believed that the number nine mystically affected his life. He was born on October 9 (as was his son Sean), and he lived at 9 Newcastle Road. Brian Epstein discovered the Beatles on 9 November 1961, and clinched a record contract for them on 9 May 1962. Lennon met Yoko Ono on 9 November, and when he was shot dead in 1980, his body was taken to Roosevelt Hospital – on New York's Ninth Avenue.

Although Lennon died on 8 December, the 5-hour time difference meant it was actually the 9th in Liverpool. On that same cold morning, within a minute of the Ex-Beatle's death, a fifty-six-year-old man died in Fazakerley Hospital. His name was also John Lennon. He died in Ward 9, and Fazakerley Hospital's postal area is Liverpool 9.

Now, back in 1895, at a pub called the Chanticleer on Athol Street, an Irish-Liverpudlian banjo-playing musician of some repute often played in a trio. This popular trio was made up of penny whistle player Jack Jones of Scotland Road, banjo-playing fishmonger John Lennon of Latimer Street, and Chandler James McCartney of Walton, who was an able pub pianist. This Lennon and McCartney predated the world-famous song-writing duo, John Lennon and James Paul McCartney, by sixty-seven years.

Let us remain in north Liverpool but go back a little further in time to witness even more strange coincidences. At Number 20 Nursery Street, off Scotland Road, in 1876, there lived a policeman's wife named Mary Nickle. She was a very dextrous and creative woman who, with endless patience, could create miniature models of ships from scraps of wood and paper which she then painstakingly placed inside of a bottle. She also carefully rolled up playing cards in such a way as to place entire decks inside the bottles, and Mary sold her bottled curios to pub landlords wishing to exhibit the unusual items on the shelves of their establishments.

In December 1876, Mrs Nickle created a replica of the *SS Bavaria*, which was sailing from Liverpool to New Orleans. The ship was expertly placed inside a bottle using long-armed tongs and a secret technique which Mary had learned from her grandfather. She then left the house to go to the corner shop, and when she returned, she saw that the bottled ship had been smashed into the coals of the fire, and the scattered wooden pieces, which she had so skillfully crafted, were all ablaze. Mary's daughter was out of the house at the time, and her husband was laid up in bed with a stomach complaint, and anyway, neither of them would have damaged the ship in a bottle because Mary's work contributed to their livelihood. So who on earth had thrown the ship in the fire?

Two months later, the *SS Bavaria* was on its way back to Liverpool from New Orleans when it was destroyed by a mysterious fire at sea, echoing the minor domestic tragedy back in Liverpool. Mary then created a model of another Liverpool ship and placed it in the bottle – and it was also found smashed. Soon afterwards the ship which the model represented was then lost at sea.

This eerie spate of dark coincidences continued for several years, until, in 1884, Mary created a miniature replica of the reformatory ship *Clarence*. The ship and its bottle were once more found mysteriously smashed and smouldering on the fire, and on the following day, the real *Clarence* was destroyed in a blaze which burnt the vessel at the water's edge in the Mersey.

After that weird happenstance, Mary decided that enough was enough and she bottled no more ships.

STRANGE BEDFELLOWS

Most of us, when we either rent or buy an old house or flat, do not spare a moment's thought for those who have inhabited the premises before us. We fill it with our own possessions and simply adjust to the fact that it is our home. Of course, this is a rather short-sighted view, for most buildings outlive their occupants by many years and even if we buy the premises, in real terms we are really only borrowing it for a time. For many people this fact is brought home to them in the most dramatic way when an ex-resident of the house or flat decides to make an unwanted appearance.

At a block of flats overlooking Sefton Park, a fifty-five-year-old resident named Frank literally had a brush with the supernatural at a quarter to four on the morning of Monday, 20 February 2006, when he got out of bed to go to the toilet. The light in the hallway was on as usual, and as Frank left his bedroom, he was more than a little surprised to see a small old woman, dressed in black, standing at the end of the hall near the front door. She was gazing intently at a particular spot on the floor, seemingly oblivious to his presence.

Frank recoiled in fright at the sight of the strange old lady, and shouted: "Hey, who are you?" The woman turned slowly and walked into the spare bedroom – but there was no sign of her when Frank followed her into the room.

On the following night, Frank came home at 11.15pm after a visit to his sister's house, and almost collided with the phantom old woman in black as he reached out to turn on the hallway light. She actually brushed against him this time, and Frank even heard her feet pattering by on the carpet, but once again the ghost vanished into the spare bedroom without a trace. Understandably, Frank is not too keen on staying at his flat after these encounters, and at the time of writing he is lodging at his sister's house. The identity of the ghostly old lady is unknown, but perhaps she is a former resident who has some unfinished business at the flat. Whoever she turns out to be, Frank is not prepared to share his house with her.

~

At around that same period, at a house on Formosa Drive in Fazakerley, another night-time apparition was playing havoc with a different family.

On the night of 14 February 2006, at one o'clock in the morning, an eleven-year-old boy who shares his bedroom with his younger brother, awoke to find a weird hooded figure in a long cowl-like garment prowling around his room. The figure went to the bed of the younger brother and stooped down over him, apparently examining the sleeping child's face very closely. The boy who witnessed this was naturally terrified, and froze when he saw the sinister figure then turn towards him and approach his bed. He closed his eyes tightly to block out the image, but could hear the apparition breathing closely by his ear. After a heart-stopping minute or so, the figure backed away towards the wardrobe in the corner of the room and evaporated into the darkness.

At first the boy's parents thought he had simply experienced a nightmare, until a visitor to the house came across the same monastic-looking figure standing at the top of the stairs. Inside the voluminous hood, a pale disfigured face was visible. Without warning, the figure suddenly seemed to flit at high speed into a corner and vanish.

The identity of this apparition is also unidentified at the moment.

~

Another bedroom mystery unfolded that very month when a young mum we shall call Danielle had a very bizarre and alarming experience at her home on Walton Lane.

On the Sunday afternoon of 19 February 2006, Danielle went in search of her little four-year-old boy Luke. She had definitely seen him going upstairs a short time before and had heard him go into his room to play with his many toys. She climbed the stairs to see what was troubling him because she could plainly hear him calling for her from inside the room and he sounded quite distressed. Imagine her alarm then, when she reached his small bedroom, yet could not find him anywhere. The boy's increasingly frantic cries seemed to be coming from underneath his bed, yet when Danielle searched the small space under the bed, she found nothing, other than the odd discarded sock.

Danielle became frantic. She could hear Luke crying out for her and yet was unable to locate him in his tiny room. In desperation she called her mother on her mobile phone to tell her about the situation and ask for advice, when, before her very eyes, the little missing boy suddenly emerged from under the bed, and started to sob hysterically.

When questioned later, the boy gave a garbled account of how he "got lost" under the bed, and the mystery then deepened in a very sinister way when Danielle was cleaning her child's room on the following afternoon, because she found a toy under the bed that she had never set eyes on before – a girl's doll. She was not one of those modern mothers who believe that the sexes should be treated equally where toys are concerned and Luke certainly did not possess a doll of any kind. He had never shown the least interest in dolls or anything more girly than an Action Man. So how the doll came to be in Luke's room remains a mystery, and Danielle was so spooked by the wretched toy, that she didn't want it in the house and gave it to me.

I consulted an expert who collects dolls, and all he could tell me was that the toy figure was made around the late sixties or early seventies.

THE SADDEST WORD IN THE WORLD

O ne sunny spring morning in 1909, at a ward in Liverpool's Southern Hospital, four men sat up in their newly-made apple-pie beds. The young nurse on duty, Sarah Jones, had just brought each of them a tray of breakfast, and she casually inquired of one of the patients about the contents of a letter he was reading.

"Oh, it's from my son Albert, love," Mr Lipson said, looking over a pair of pince-nez perched on the end of his wide ruddy nose. "His application to join the Thames Police was successful. I should imagine it won't be long before he's a detective at Scotland Yard."

"Oh, really?" said Nurse Jones, carefully laying the tray of porridge, toast and cocoa on Mr Lipson's lap. She enjoyed chatting to her patients – there were men from every walk of life on the ward, and they each had a story to tell – and she saw it as an important part of her job to listen to them.

"He moved to London a year ago," continued Lipson, "and he's due to be married in July."

"Ah, that's nice, Mr Lipson, bet you're really proud of him, aren't you?" said the nurse kindly, before leaving his bedside for the ward kitchen.

The rough-diamond in the bed next to Mr Lipson was Billy McCann, a costermonger recovering from a stomach operation.

"My lad's an apprentice at Cammell-Laird's over in Tranmere, like," McCann boasted. "He worked on that *Ugazali* steamship for the Peruvians, and he's working on something very top secret for the Navy at the moment, but I'm not allowed to say what, like."

McCann was just about to over-elaborate on the details of the supposedly hush-hush naval project, when Mr Blackhouse, the manager of a public house on Old Hall Street, let out what seemed to be a deliberately induced cough. When he had recovered from the fleeting bronchial attack, Blackhouse took his turn to boast.

"All my sons have done well for themselves, but my youngest son is only fourteen and he has his future mapped out for him already, I'm telling you. He wants to be a barrister, and he already knows the law inside out. He can argue black is white, and wins every argument, he does, and you should see his handwriting, a real scholar, he is. Takes after his mother; has her brains."

The nurse had returned from the kitchen just in time to hear the tail end of the publican's account of his brainy son, and she and the three patients then glanced towards Mr Roccardo, a distinguished-looking silvery-haired man in his fifties, who was gazing out of the window as he rested on his pillows. He suddenly noticed the expectant looks of the three men and the nurse and realised that it was his turn to say something, so he did. He told of his beautiful twenty-year-old son, Joseph Roccardo, a real gentleman who had already made a fortune in the diamond fields of South Africa. He bred racehorses, was an accomplished pianist, and lived in a beautiful ivory-white mansion in leafy Cheshire.

"Joseph was born in 1889, and from the moment I set eyes on him in my wife's arms, I knew he was destined for great things," said Mr Roccardo, with a tear in his eye.

Young Sarah blushed and asked if Joseph was married. Mr Roccardo said he wasn't, and with a wry smile told the nurse that she would be sure to fall in love with him if she saw him in the flesh.

"Oh! Go on! What would he see in me? I'm just a nurse," Sarah said despondently.

"A nurse is a noble person, and you're beautiful, Sarah," was Mr Roccardo's sincere-sounding reply.

Mr Roccardo was discharged from hospital on the following day, and that weekend, Sarah Jones took a shortcut through St James's Cemetery with another nurse named Mary. Glancing at the names of the dead on the headstones as she passed them by, one inscription jumped out at her and caused her to halt in her tracks. It read: JOSEPH ROCCARDO 1889-1889 – and below this the inscription said that the boy had lived for just fifteen minutes.

A tear rolled down Sarah's cheek, and she and Mary continued on their way. The saddest word in the world: 'If'.

TWO DEVILISH TALES

People often ask me if there are any supernatural stories that really scare me and keep me awake at night. Well, the following true tales have definitely played on my mind, and they all feature that hoary old character we know as the Devil, who, by all accounts, is as active today as he was in the Garden of Eden.

In the 1970s, at a flat in a tenement called Sidney Gardens, in the Edge Hill district of Liverpool, a boy whom I shall call Joseph (not his real name), lived with his aunt, who I shall call Edna.

At the age of eleven, Joseph tragically died through solvent abuse, and his aunt found his body lying on his bed in his room one morning when she went to get him up for school. Although his body was already cold and stiff, Edna couldn't believe the evidence of her own eyes that the boy was dead – she hadn't even known that he was experimenting with solvents – and she futilely tried to shake the boy awake as if he were just sleeping.

She had been an ardent Catholic for most of her life, but had experienced a lapse in her faith in recent months, and she shook her fist at the crucifix on the wall and started to swear. She screamed at God for answers. Why had He taken Joseph away, the most precious thing she had in the world? As she was cursing and railing at the cross, a dark silhouette flitted past the frosted glass of the window that looked on to the tenement landing. Then came the sound of faint footsteps in the hallway, which quickly brought her to her senses, because the front door had definitely been shut. A tall man, dressed entirely in black, with unusually long arms and a small head, came into the bedroom, and stared at the dead boy's aunt with eerie dark-ringed eyes.

Somehow, the woman intuitively knew who the man in black was – the Devil. The crucifix clattered off the wall and bounced under the bed. The boy's aunt ran to the dark figure and begged him to bring Joseph back from the dead, and the man agreed but with one stipulation; he would have to take a soul as payment for the resurrection. Edna loved her nephew so much that she was prepared to promise anything, and she foolishly offered her own soul to the Devil as payment. The Devil then placed an odd-looking hand on the boy's face and she noticed that all his fingers were an identical length.

The Devil's touch had an immediate and powerful effect; Joseph's body lurched and convulsed violently for a while, as if an electric current had been passed through it. Then the boy opened his eyes and smiled, and his aunt threw her arms around him and smothered him with kisses. She turned to thank the dark stranger – but he had already gone.

Unfortunately, Joseph did not seem to have learned any lessons from his uncomfortable brush with death. His behaviour changed for the worse not long afterwards and he was soon expelled from nearby St Anne's School. His aunt soon realised that the Joseph who had returned from the dead bore no resemblance personality-wise to the Joseph she had known before, who, although he was no angel, had his heart in the right place. This new Joseph had no respect for anyone or anything and living with him became a nightmare.

Aunt Edna died some months later from a mysterious illness, possibly brought on by the enormous stress she had been under, and the orphaned boy still hung around the area and lived rough on the streets. Social Services tried in vain to take the boy into their custody for his own protection, but he was impossible to tie down and always seemed to vanish within hours of being placed in foster care.

The eleven-year-old was seen by many people over the years in the Edge Hill area, hanging round street corners, generally up to no good, and the baffling thing was that he never aged. After St Anne's School was demolished, he was often seen prowling around the ruins of the old schoolyard after dark. I myself once lived in the area where this tale was said to have taken place, I had heard of this story, and always dreaded meeting the boy who couldn't, or wouldn't, grow up when I passed St Anne's school on the way to my friend's house.

~

In 2005, a fervently religious layman named Sam, from a certain church in the North West, spent all his spare time calling door-to-door at houses on Merseyside in the hope of converting people to his faith. No matter how many knockbacks he received, or how many doors were slammed in his face, Sam soldiered on with his self-imposed mission to convert as many people as possible before he died.

One evening, Sam called at a house off Brown's Lane, Netherton, and was pleased to be invited in by a distinguished-looking man. However, his host was soon putting forward a series of powerful anti-religious arguments, claiming that God was wrong and the Devil was right. The man could quote whole sections of both the Old and New Testaments, as well as Apocrypha, in support of his theories and Sam sensed that there was something deeply sinister about him.

Feeling distinctly uncomfortable and out of his depth, Sam made up a feeble excuse to leave, upon which the man turned on the television and Sam became intrigued to see an episode of the old sitcom *Steptoe and Son* that he had never seen before. Sam was a fan of the series and knew every episode virtually by heart. He therefore stayed and watched the programme as the opinionated fanatic continued to praise Satan.

Sam started to suspect the man of being the Devil in disguise, and he seriously wondered whether he had even conjured up the episode of *Steptoe and Son* just to keep him there. As soon as Sam turned over those bizarre thoughts in his mind, the characters on the screen stopped acting and froze – they turned outwards from the television to look at him accusingly. Sam's stomach turned somersaults and he immediately leapt to his feet and pushed past the man without making eye contact, determined not to fall under his evil spell again. This seemed to amuse the man, who started laughing in such an eerie way, that Sam could feel the hairs rising on the nape of his neck. He fled that house in such haste that he left a pile of his pamphlets scattered in the hallway.

Sam had found the whole encounter deeply troubling, but something inside him compelled him to revisit the house in Netherton on the following night. He had no intention of going in and re-enacting his experiences of the previous night, but he just needed to take another look at it. Perhaps it was just idle curiosity, but he could not explain it, even to himself.

Imagine how he felt then when he arrived in front of the house again only to find it in total darkness, with no curtains at any of the windows, the gardens overgrown, seemingly uninhabited. When he made enquiries with one of the neighbours he was told that no one had lived in that house for at least four months!

MYSTICAL HELPER

On the morning of Saturday, 21 November 1846, the people of Liverpool were recovering from one of the most violent storms in living memory. Ships at the docks had been torn from their moorings and smashed against the wharves, houses were shorn of slates and thatching, steeples had been knocked crooked, and chimneys swept away. The raging tempest had started with a strange display of coloured lightning over Liverpool Bay, followed by sightings of a waterspout off the Crosby coast. Furthermore, curious reports of 'unearthly sounds', likened to voices singing and howling, were heard over Birkenhead and were interpreted by the superstitious as omens of impending doom.

Against the backdrop of the storm-wrecked town, an intriguing and mysterious character came into prominence, but his true identity and his origins are still as mysterious today as they were then. This individual looked for all the world like an itinerant monk; for he was clad in a monk's brown cowl and had a long white beard above which was a pair of the most piercing, hypnotic eyes. He always had with him a basket laden with bread, herbs and talismans, and carried a cross-headed staff. Yet he did not belong to any religious order or brotherhood and called himself simply Clarn. When asked to describe himself he would enigmatically say, "I am a man of no religion, who recognised a force older than the stars," and leave his questioner to ponder on what he had said.

Clarn first appeared in the south of Liverpool, where, with a show of superhuman strength, he lifted a huge fallen beam from a woman who had been trapped under the ruins of a dilapidated cottage hit by the storm. During the course of the night, the strange mystic also fed dozens of people left homeless by the storm by producing a seemingly never-ending supply of bread and hot, sweet-tasting meats from inside his basket. Clarn was viewed with great suspicion by the local priest, who believed the 'monk' was nothing more than a sleight-of-hand conjurer. Clarn, however, just sighed, as if the man's ignorance was something he came across every day – a cross he had to bear – and patiently went on to explain that Angliolo Paoli, an eighteenth century Italian saint, had shown him how to multiply food for the poor in Rome, in 1714 – one hundred and thirty-two years before!

The priest stormed off in a huff, his cassock flying, after he had heard this seemingly outrageous statement, dismissing Clarn as a downright charlatan. However, an old woman timidly came forward in Liverpool, who said that she recognised the enigmatic sage as the same man who had miraculously produced corn for the granary of a convent fifty years before, and that, amazingly, he had hardly aged at all.

When Clarn was attacked by two robbers near the Brownlow Hill Workhouse some weeks later, his usual meek demeanour was exchanged for that of a fierce warrior. In a brief but spectacular show of fighting skills, he left both of his assailants lying unconscious by the use of an extraordinary form of pugilism. From eye witness statements it would seem that it was very similar to karate.

In 1847 Clarn somehow gained admittance to the Lunatic Hospital and Asylum on Ashton Street, where he cured several patients of madness by the laying on of hands. That was until his activities were discovered by James Parker, the governor of the asylum, who immediately ordered him off the premises. His unorthodox methods smelt of witchcraft and undermined the asylum's policy of control and containment, with no attempt at understanding or trying to find a cure for the inmates' interminable misery and suffering.

Not long after that, a plague of cholera swept through Liverpool like a tidal wave, leaving over fifteen thousand people dead in its wake. Fever sheds were opened on Mount Pleasant to cope with the casualties; in effect they were just places where the cholera victims were left to die. Amongst those in the population who had managed to stay free of the disease, only the bravest were prepared to care for those who ended up in the sheds. Clarn was one such and was said to have cured several children who had been abandoned by their families to die there. Once again, instead of being praised for his selflessness and amazing medical skills, the Church viewed the miracle-worker as a possible Christian dissident, and hounded him out of Lancashire.

Then came the incredible tale of how, when Clarn was cornered like a hunted animal by the authorities in the village of Hale, he made a dash for the shore, then, in front of his astonished pursuers, actually walked over the river to the Cheshire side. Having made his escape, he lived for a while where Weston Point is now located. Clarn then vanished into obscurity and was reduced to something of a folklore character.

Was Clarn some kind of sophisticated confidence trickster, or was he a mystical helper with genuine magical powers?

STICK-MAN

At her house in Everton Valley, on the Tuesday afternoon of 30 November 1937, sixteen-year-old Susan Williams was sitting up in bed, suffering from a dreadful cold, trying to read that American favourite, *Little Women*. Despite the book's huge popularity on both sides of the Atlantic, Susan just couldn't get into it – perhaps it was because she felt so unwell and couldn't concentrate properly.

The November sunlight of the late afternoon shone through a gap in the centre of the drawn curtains, throwing a luminous line lengthwise down Susan's face. For some subconscious reason, she dropped the book on the floor at the side of the bed, and her thoughts turned to the age-old subject of ghosts. Perhaps it was just the fever playing tricks on her mind, but the girl had a growing suspicion that she was being watched by something or something. The more she thought about it the more she could detect the presence, until she felt a cold steely shiver crawl up her back. She lifted the sleeve of her nightgown and found that her arms were covered with goose-pimples – a sure sign that spirits were near, according to an old superstition. Her face felt hot and flushed, and she could have sworn that she'd heard a floorboard creak in the room, so she hid beneath the covers for a while, too afraid to even shout out for her grandmother, who was downstairs in the kitchen preparing a pot of Irish stew.

After a short while, the temperature proved to be too intense under the blankets; better to face a ghost than to sweat and choke in the unbearable clammy heat. She poked her head out, revealing droplets of sweat on her face, and could see no one in the room. A raucous screech suddenly pierced the air, and the enormous shadow of a seagull in flight flitted across the sunlit curtains, startling Susan out of her wits. She swore at the silly bird, but was inwardly relieved that it had been nothing worse, then reached under her pillow for a handkerchief. She blew her nose for what seemed like the hundredth time that day, and heard a low-pitched buzzing tone in her right ear; the product of the head cold.

Susan got up, put on her slippers, then sat listlessly on the edge of the bed. She gazed out of focus at the threadbare carpet and sank into a daydream, which was interrupted by a voice from nowhere, which almost caused the teenager to faint. Close to her ear, an old woman's voice gasped, "Get out of this room!"

Susan needed no second invitation, she sprinted to the door, pulled it open, and ran down the stairs crying out in alarm. Old Mrs Williams, her grandmother, scolded her when she barged into the kitchen, skidding to a halt just in front of the stove. With a lot of tutting, her grandmother pushed the handle of the stew pot away from her excitable charge.

"Susan, dear. What on earth's the matter?"

"I've just heard a ghost in my room, Granny!" panted Susan, embracing the astonished old woman and burying her face in her cooking pinafore. "It was definitely a ghost. It was really creepy and told me to get out of my room."

Granny Williams felt Susan's forehead with the back of her hand.

"You've got a temperature, you poor thing, that's all. It can make you imagine all kinds of things. Come and drink some distilled water."

Susan shook her head and tried to describe the disembodied voice that had floated out of mid-air with the warning to leave the room, but she started to cough and splutter and gave up with an exhausted sigh.

"Oooh! I think you need some goosegrease on brown paper m'girl," said her gran, always ready to resort to her old tried and trusted health remedies.

That evening, the Williams family and Mrs Jones from next door were gathered in the parlour around the fire, and the talk was of ghosts. Susan sat between her mother and older sister Annie on the sofa as her father related the story of a terrifying fire-breathing phantom which he had seen when he was a lad, many years ago on Erskine Street. The ghost had been the horrifying shade of Enzo, a Victorian circus performer, sword-swallower and fire-eater extraordinaire, whose head literally exploded at the Shakespeare Theatre on Fraser Street when he attempted the highly dangerous Human Volcano fire-breathing act.

"Enzo filled his mouth from a flagon of inflammable spirit, and he stood there, gazing at the audience to the sound of a drum-roll," said Mr Williams, his pipe bobbing up and down from the corner of his mouth. "Anyway, I was sitting in the front row with my dad, and Enzo held up this type of candle. He seemed to cough, causing the stuff in his mouth to trickle down his chin, and all of a sudden I saw this blue flame under his lips. He frantically tried to wipe the flame away with his hand but suddenly there was an enormous flash, followed by this loud bang, and his face exploded, sending flaming gobbets of flesh all over the stage. Ooh! It was the worst thing I've ever seen. What was left of his head became one big fireball, and I'm not sure if that killed him, but he fell down on his knees, and the flames dripped down the front of his jacket and the drum-roll stopped. Next thing I heard all these screams and my father said, 'Come on, lad,' and he dragged me out of the place. There was a big crush in the audience because I think everyone panicked and thought the fire was going to spread. I'll never forget that horrible smell of someone burning and the way that fire engulfed him."

"Oh! That's terrible," Marge Jones said, her face between her hands. "I've never heard the likes."

"I haven't finished yet," said Mr Williams, and he continued his colourful story. "That winter, I was playing on Erskine Street with Tommy Bristow, and the roads were like black glass. Very icy. Anyroad, this rumour went round that Enzo's ghost had been seen in an alleyway off Manfred Street that evening. That's where he lived, the circus fellah who burnt to death. Ask Tommy Bristow about this if you see him, Marge, he's got a better memory than me.

"Me and Tommy were mucking about on Manfred Street, and if you know that street you'll know it's badly lit even now, and I'm going back forty years, when it was even darker. We saw this light, right down the bottom of the alleyway, and it was getting nearer. Then we noticed this figure of a lad running towards us. As he got nearer I recognised him. It was Johnny Wright, a lad from Prescot, a right tearaway. And he was running away from someone as if his life depended on it. Next minute, me and Tommy saw what he was running from, alright – a huge man, breathing out flames. Next thing, we're trying to run on this black ice, slipping all over the place. Johnny Wright flew straight past us, and you should have seen the look of blind terror on his face. We eventually managed to get a grip on the ice and ran from Erskine Street right down Islington to Canterbury Street, where we saw this copper. We were surprised when we told him about Enzo's ghost because he didn't seem to doubt us for a minute, as if he knew something as well. 'Well you'd best be getting home then!' he says."

"Did anyone else see the ghost, Dad?" Susan asked.

"Dozens of people did," said Mr Williams, in a matter-of-fact way. "They reckon he wasn't at rest because his wife was carrying on with someone before he was even buried. I'll never forget that night. I saw Enzo's ghost and I'd swear on a stack of Bibles that I did."

The ghost stories went on till midnight, and Susan was so afraid of sleeping in the room where she had heard the old woman's voice, that she persuaded her sister Annie to let her sleep in her bed. That night, Susan had horrific nightmares about Enzo's exploding head and his blackened, charred body lying on the stage. At two-thirty that morning she awoke in the middle of one of these nightmares, and found herself unable to move for a moment. She turned and clung to Annie, who was still sleeping soundly. After tossing and turning for a while, Susan sank into a deep sleep, during which a heart-stopping nightmare played in her mind. In it, she looked out of her bedroom window and saw a man in the yard, gazing up at her. His body was completely charred, and only the whites of his eyes and his teeth stood out against his dark form. His carbon-black body looked almost stick-like, as if only the skeleton had remained after the flesh and muscle had been roasted away.

This time, Susan awakened with a loud shriek which startled Annie out of her pleasant sleep. She told her about the sickeningly realistic nightmare, but Annie, who was none too pleased to be woken up, told her to go back to sleep after glancing at the bedside clock. It was 4.15am. That dream of the grotesquely carbonised stick-man recurred on three consecutive nights.

Then, on Monday, 6 December 1937, something took place which chilled Susan Williams to her marrow. Shortly before 10 o'clock that morning, as a dense fog blanketed most of Liverpool, twenty-year-old trainee RAF pilot, Gordon Dutton Angus, was circling the skies of the city after leaving the Sealand airbase near Chester, when disaster struck. The plane suddenly lost altitude for some reason, and as it sped towards the ground, its undercarriage missed the roof of Everton Valley Convent by inches. Instead, a millisecond later, the plane hit the roof of a Presbyterian church, then slanted down 150 yards in a fatal nosedive. Eye-witness Thomas Goulding held his breath as he saw the pilot desperately trying to scramble out of the plane, with his leg over the side of the cockpit, but before he had a chance to jump, the craft hit a series of backyard walls and exploded into a fierce fireball as the fuel tank was ruptured. The nose of the plane landed in the yard of Number 25, Everton Valley Road, and the tail section smashed into Number 2 Kirkdale Road.

A mother and daughter would almost certainly have been killed that morning, but survived through a curious twist of fate. They were about to go into town, and were heading for the backyard to leave via the back door, when their clubman knocked at the front door. They turned around and were in the hall, about to answer the call, when they heard an ear-splitting explosion at the back of their house which blew the roof off and demolished the kitchen walls.

A Mr Flood and a Mr Baguley fought valiantly to rescue the pilot of the crashed plane but, sadly, the intense heat of the burning aircraft kept them at bay. One destroyed house had contained furniture purchased by a man for his wedding on New Year's Day – it was smashed to firewood, and the room where he had intended to spend his honeymoon was left with no roof. Part of the bedroom where Susan Williams usually slept was also destroyed, and had the girl been in her own bed she would certainly have been killed. When Susan and her grandmother went into the backyard, they could see the tail of the plane protruding over a wall just a few houses away, surrounded by a roaring inferno. When the fire was finally extinguished, Susan watched as the ambulance men solemnly removed the pilot's body. She gasped. For she instantly recognised the very same blackened stick-man she had been having the nightmares about. The body was taken to Stanley Hospital.

Were the nightmares of the grossly-burned man simply coincidence? Or were the dreams some kind of premonition of the Everton plane crash? And what about the ghostly warning voice of the old woman in Susan's bedroom? Could that also have been a warning for Susan to vacate that bedroom before the tragedy struck?

PORTRAIT OF YAGAN.

CHIEF OF THE SWAN RIVER.

GRAVEYARD GHOSTS

hosts in graveyards are, believe it or not, something of a rarity, despite the archetypal image we have of spectres drifting about amongst lichen-encrusted tombstones after dark. Statistically, you're more likely to bump into a ghost in your own home, the workplace, or even on the road, than you are in a cemetery. Having said that, there are some phantoms haunting the cemeteries of Liverpool, and here are just a few accounts of these graveyard ghosts.

One rainy afternoon in 1986, John Butler was visiting the grave of one of his relatives at Everton Cemetery on Long Lane, Fazakerley, when he spotted a tall, half-naked, black man. He had an assortment of strange red feathers in his hair and was extremely scantily clad. The man stood stock still, rigidly gazing at Mr Butler, who was at first startled, then rather scared by the presence of this oddity, with all the distinctive facial features of an aborigine, or native Australian, who would have been more at home in the outback. "He must be frozen stiff for a start," thought Mr Butler.

He became more and more uncomfortable with being the focus of this strange fellow's attention and decided not to hang around. He ran out of the cemetery and later told his family about his creepy encounter. They scathingly questioned what such a misplaced person might be doing hanging around Everton Cemetery. The popular movie that year was *Crocodile Dundee*, which featured an aboriginal character, so no one in the Butler family, or anyone else for that matter, took the reports of the ghost seriously, even after it was seen and reported by quite a number of people. So, what exactly was behind the sightings of the ghost of an aborigine in Everton Cemetery?

Well, believe it or not, the head of a famous aborigine named Yagan was once buried in Everton Cemetery. Yagan was a fierce warrior of the Nangoon tribe which fought against British soldiers but he was killed by them in 1833. As a barbarous adjunct to the killing, they hacked off Yagan's head and skinned his back to obtain the tribal markings as a trophy. The head was then put on show at various exhibitions up and down the country and ended up at Liverpool Museum, where it started to decay. In 1964, not quite sure what to do with their grisly and increasingly smelly exhibit, the museum packed the head into a plywood box, along with two equally appalling 'treasures'; a Peruvian mummy and a Maori head. They then had them buried at Everton Cemetery at Section 16, Grave Number 296 – the exact spot where John Butler had seen the ghost of the aborigine.

In 1997, the head was reclaimed by the Noongar tribe of Australia and returned to its spiritual homeland.

~

There have been several sightings of a soldier at Everton Cemetery – one in 1969 and two more in November 1979, but whether the ghosts were World War One or World War Two soldiers could not be firmly established. A ghostly

Scottish soldier in a kilt has been seen regularly outside of Springwood Cemetery, up in Allerton, but who he was when he walked this earth as a member of the living, is still unknown.

In 2006, I received several reports of a ghost in uniform who had been seen in broad daylight in Anfield Cemetery. One of the witnesses to this ghost was Lyn Staunton, a very down-to-earth woman who runs the entertainment agency Power Promotions. Lyn was responsible for bringing Hollywood legend Mickey Rooney to Liverpool's Royal Court Theatre in May 2006, and not only was she was the first female Chairman of the Variety Club in the North West, she was re-elected for four consecutive years. Lyn is also a popular panellist on Billy Butler's *Stars in their Ears* local talent show each week on BBC Radio Merseyside.

In the summer of 2006, Lyn went to Anfield Cemetery with her mum Georgina, and she saw something highly unusual. Lyn relates her experience:

"I was visiting my father's grave with my mother in Anfield cemetery, and my father's grave is quite close to the entrance of the cemetery, near the turning after the crematorium. It was a beautiful sunny day, and I was driving into the cemetery when I saw a soldier in the distance, standing almost directly in front of me. I don't know why I was startled by the sight, but there was just something about him. He was standing to attention and looking straight ahead. I said to my mother, 'Look at that soldier.' My mother looked to where I was pointing and saw nothing. Then, after a few more seconds, he was gone.

I was not afraid at all, just intrigued. We later left the cemetery, and my mother rang me later that evening to say that her sister Ellen had told her that two soldiers were buried by the church near to my sighting and both had been awarded the Victoria Cross. I was sorry to disappoint my mother but the soldier I saw was not near the church but much further into the middle of the cemetery. The next day I went back to the cemetery, and took my mother with me. I parked my car and walked to the spot where I had seen the soldier. There was no one there, but to my utter amazement I looked down at the ground and found that I was standing in front of three soldiers' graves. The names on those graves are not British. I have, to date, not been back to the cemetery, but I do intend to investigate what happened to those soldiers. Being a woman, my ignorance regarding soldiers' uniforms is understandable, I suppose, but on each of these graves is an anchor, so what uniform would they be wearing? The anchor would certainly suggest either a sailor's or a marine."

I asked Lyn if the ghost interacted with her. Did he acknowledge her in any way? Some ghosts are not at all interactive, and either stare through the person observing them, or ignore them.

"Believe me, Tom," Lyn told me, "I saw him and he saw me."

If you too have seen this ghost in Anfield Cemetery – or any ghosts anywhere for that matter, please write to me at the address given at the end of this book and I will only be too happy to shed any light I can upon them.

THE HEADLESS HORSEMAN OF BIBBY'S LANE

Once upon a time, Bootle was a picturesque little backwater, its attractions being its clear sparkling mineral water springs and spas, golden coastal dunes, sleepy half-timbered cottages, and fields of beautiful wild flowers, over which butterflies fluttered in the summer. The cottagers grew vegetables and fruit for the market, and Bootle's pure springwater was bottled to be sold across England, and Liverpool purchased the water by the barrelful. Boltelai was the original name of this place, derived from the Anglo-Saxon words bold, bolt and botl, meaning house, dwelling, and village respectively. At one point, historians believed Bootle had been founded by the Vikings, but it existed long before they arrived on our shores. It was probably established after the Battle of Chester in 613 AD, when the Anglians of Northumbria settled there.

There is also a mysterious and supernatural side to Bootle. Beneath the very ordinary looking streets, in the sandstone rock upon which the town is built, there are great unmapped caverns, complete with stalagmites and stalactites, huge toadstools and other fungi, plus a lake measuring half a mile in both length and breadth. This vast subterranean domain has long been said to be the home of 'kobolds' – ugly-looking creatures reported all over Europe who invariably live underground. Miners in Wales, Lancashire and Cheshire have occasionally reported sightings of these grotesque-looking goblins that thrive in the Stygian darkness of caverns.

Rumours of kobolds and other 'intra-terrestrials' deep beneath the clay and bedrock of the North West are thought to have been started by Irish and Welsh settlers in the 1840s. However, long before that, in archaic English folklore, there are accounts to be found which describe faerie mounds and various species of gnomes and cluricaune who occasionally emerge from wells and caves in which they live.

Today in Bootle, there are places which hint at the existence of the underground lake which exists hundreds of feet below the streets. The clues are to be found in Waterworks Street, Spring Cove and Well Lane, and of course, the staggering two thousand recorded springs of Bootle.

Next we come to Bootle ghosts, the stories of which would fill many books, so let us concentrate on just one of the more spectacular tales, of a frightening spectre known as the Headless Horseman of Bibby's Lane. Our story begins in the autumn of 1900, as wraiths of yellow fog infiltrate the gaslit streets of the expanding town and clothe everything in their unearthly mantle. Ships' horns groan ominously on the Mersey, and a full moon can just be detected trying to penetrate the gathering mists upon this Monday evening of 8 October.

Bootle bootmaker Billy Hutchings of Peel Road, called upon his relative Patrick Whelan of Boswell Street, and found him hunched over the grate looking pale, ill and trembling as he tried repeatedly to start his coal fire. The lit taper in his hand shook so badly that Billy had to light the fire himself.

"Whatever is the matter, Patrick?" Billy asked his cousin, and knelt on the hearthrug, rubbing his palms together over the flickering flames.

After a thoughtful pause, Patrick Whelan said, "I saw a ghost, Billy, as clear as you're kneeling there."

"A ghost?" Billy said with a chuckle in his voice, but his eyes betrayed what he was really thinking, which was that Patrick was giving a very good impression of someone who had indeed just seen a ghost.

"About twenty minutes ago," said Patrick, leaning on the mantelpiece and eyeing the clock. "I was walking up Bibby's Lane from work, and there wasn't a soul about; no, I tell a lie, that old blind match-seller, Mrs Hughes, was there and she heard it too."

"*Heard* the ghost?" asked Billy leaping up and looking into Patrick's eyes. What he saw there was naked fear.

"Yes, yes, hear me out, Billy," said Patrick impatiently. "I heard this clip-clop of a horse somewhere behind me and I turned around, and there was this man, dressed in real old-fashioned clothes, with gauntlets and long boots and a long coat." Patrick shuddered and then took several deep breaths before saying, "And I thought he was leaning forward at first, because I couldn't see his head, but then I realised he … he … didn't have one … just this horrible bony stump

112

sticking out of the top of his coat. It was enough to make you sick."

"No head? That's impossible!"

Billy Hutchings was particularly unnerved because his forty-seven-year-old cousin was the most sceptical, hard-headed, down-to-earth man he knew. He was a tough dock labourer who had no time for ghost stories or anything to do with the supernatural, and so for him to say that he had seen a headless man on Bibby's Lane chilled the bootmaker to the marrow.

After a spell of grim reflection, Patrick gasped, "Ugh! That bony thing must have been the top of his spine."

"What did he do?" Billy asked, with a growing dark fascination.

"He rode straight past me, with his cloak fluttering out behind him, and he vanished into the fog by that baker's shop – what's the name of that place?"

"Blackledge's ... Blackledge's the bakers," replied Billy with a dry mouth.

Yes, just around the corner from your house, Billy," said Patrick. "He just vanished, disappeared, him and the horse, and the blind woman raised her head in a quizzical way, because she must have heard the sounds of that horse's shoes on the cobbles come to an abrupt end. I'll ask her when I next see her, I was too flabberghasted at the time."

Billy Hutchings slid a flask of whiskey from the inside pocket of his jacket, took a swig, then offered it to his dazed cousin. Patrick took two swigs, wiped his mouth, then said, "I hope this is not some kind of omen, Billy."

Don't read things into these strange incidents, Patrick, it's not for us to comment on or interpret," Billy said, and he gestured for the return of his flask and was given it. "These type of things are to do with the Devil; his idea of a joke."

"That bone, it was horrible, just sticking up there," Patrick muttered, gazing into the blue and yellow flames of the new fire.

"Go and see a priest," was Billy's advice.

That evening, Billy Hutchings went to the local pub, and mentioned nothing about his cousin's eerie experience, but just sat in a corner by the fireplace, listening to an elderly character named Old John, who was softly singing an old ballad. In between the lyrics of the song, a word drifted in from the conversation of three men standing at the bar. That word caught Billy's ears and startled him. That word was 'ghost'.

The bootmaker quickly left the inglenook and moved over until he was within earshot of the three men, and to his astonishment, they were talking about a headless man on horseback.

113

"Excuse me there, gentlemen, but I couldn't help overhearing the talk of ghosts just then," Billy said, and with a smile he ingratiated himself into the trio's company.

He learned from the men, who lived on nearby Keats Street, that a bricklayer named Roberts had seen the terrifying apparition of a headless horseman on Bibby's Lane at five o'clock that morning, as he set out for work. Roberts had found himself directly in the path of the horseman as he sped down the lane out of a heavy morning mist. Sparks had flown off the shoes of the horse as it raced across the cobbles, and the animal and its unearthly rider had narrowly missed the bricklayer.

Billy Hutchings just didn't know what to think when he heard this and his head began to swim. When closing time loomed, he waited for an elderly shopkeeper named Tom Berrington – who lived close to the bootmaker's home – to finish his drink, then walked home with him. As the sixty-eight-year-old Mr Berrington walked out of the pub with Billy, he curled a long scarf around the lower half of his face and braced himself against the now freezing fog. Billy Hutchings was shivering, partly from the cold, but mostly from his fear of meeting the horserider with no head, and he walked along, gazing at the pavement, afraid to look up in case he came face to face with the ghost. Before long, Mr Berrington reached his home at Number 1 Boswell Street, and bid goodnight to the bootmaker, who had to walk along the deserted fogbound street for just a short distance to his own home at Number 61 Peel Road. Billy was just inserting the key in the door when he heard something in the distance, indistinct at first, then getting louder and louder – the unmistakable sound of galloping hooves, heading in his direction!

He could not bring himself to turn round and look at the source of that ominous galloping sound, which, by now he could feel beneath his feet. With fingers which felt as useless as uncooked sausages, he rattled the key in the lock, desperately trying to open the door. The horse was suddenly thundering upon Billy, and a split second before he lunged into the safety of his hallway, he momentarily stole a glance to left, and confirmed that it was indeed a lone rider upon a dark horse, now less than thirty feet away, and the horseman was riding on the pavement. Whether he was headless or not, Billy had not been able to tell with such a quick glance. Billy slammed the door and threw himself on the hall floor as the horse and its maniacal rider pounded past. Within the minute, the people of the street were opening their doors after hearing the

114

horseman thunder past at such a late hour, and at such speed.

As in many close communities, news in Bootle spread like wildfire and now the sinister story of the headless horseman had reached the ears of most of the folk in the neighbourhood, and a panic spread. For a long time afterwards, after dark, and even in the early twilight hours – especially when a fog from Liverpool Bay rolled over the area – the superstitious people of Bootle lived in mortal dread of meeting the headless horseman.

Speculation about the identity of the ghost was rife, with ever more bizarre and mysterious suggestions being put forward by the day. Some said he was one of the long-awaited Horsemen of the Apocalypse, whilst others were positive that he was none other than Old Nick himself, out to take sinners on a hell-ride as punishment for their wicked sins. Some of the older people of the neighbourhood had heard of the headless horseman in their own childhood, and their parents had told them that the spectre was restless and agitated because he was searching for his head.

A Scotsman who lived near to Billy Hutchings told how the MacLaine clan of Lochbuie in Scotland were also cursed by a headless horseman who had been seen by many people over the years because of an ancient curse. The Scot advised all those sitting round, enthralled by his tale, to sleep with crucifixes on their front doors, for surely the horseman was an agent of the Devil on a mission to collect the souls of the decadent.

The manifestations of the ghost seemed to be mostly centred on Bibby's Lane, but twelve-year-old Ginny Kelly of Chaucer Street said she witnessed the materialisation of the ghost near St Leonard's Church at the junction of Bibby's Lane and Peel Road. Was there some significance in this? One person who definitely thought there was, was Miss Ellen Petty, a sixty-seven-year-old Irishwoman living on Rimrose Road. Miss Petty was said to be a medium, and she 'sensed' that the menacing ghost on horseback was the spirit of an innocent man who had been lynched by a mob on Bibby's Lane a hundred years before. The ghost was active now because it was the anniversary of his murder at the hands of the vigilantes, who had suspected him of the murder of a child. They had hanged him from a tree, then decapitated him and left his head on show as a deterrent to others who would harm a child. The medium gazed into the coals of her fire and said she could see the crowd putting the body of the headless man on his horse before letting the animal ride through the town with the corpse strapped to the saddle.

As the weeks wore on, the encounters with the phantom rider diminished, and by December, heavy blizzards distracted most people from pondering on the uncanny goings-on which had taken place in the autumn.

In the 1960s and 70s, the headless horseman once again returned to haunt Bibby's Lane and other parts of Bootle, this time for just a few days, and again it was during the autumn when he put in his spine-chilling appearances, on one occasion terrifying a boy delivering the morning papers. Was Ellen Petty right? Was the apparition the restless shade of an innocent man who had found himself on the rough end of mob justice? It's hard to say unless we find a headless skeleton in the area of Bibby's Lane. We may discover more one day, as many of these mysteries have a habit of resolving themselves eventually.

Over the years, another phantom of the road has been seen on Bibby's Lane; that of a ghostly coach and horses, which I have written about elsewhere in the *Haunted Liverpool* series. At this time, I cannot say whether this apparition is connected to the headless horseman or not.

IGGY

One afternoon in 2006 I caught a hackney cab home from town, and during the course of the journey, the driver, a Broadgreen man named James Lamb, related a very strange story to me. At the age of two-and-a-half, James Lamb junior, the cabby's son, underwent a life-saving heart transplant at a hospital in Newcastle-upon-Tyne. The heart which young James received was from a German child who had died in a traffic accident in Germany; that is all Mr Lamb knows about the donor who gave his son the gift of life. Little James made a steady recovery, but his father soon noticed intriguing aspects of the boy's behaviour which had not been evident before his operation. James often talked to someone invisible in the corner of the living room, and when his dad would ask the child who he was talking to, he would always say "Iggy".

As the child got older, his descriptions of the unseen Iggy became more detailed. James said Iggy was an 'army man', but naturally, his father surmised that this character was just one of those imaginary friends some children dream up – until Iggy was seen by two other people. James Lamb senior says, "My two nephews stayed at the house one night, and they came running upstairs white as sheets and said there was a man dressed in uniform in the living room. They refuse to stay at the house now."

Not long afterwards, James senior was in bed when he heard a loud bang down in the living room. He thought a burglar was breaking in and ran downstairs wielding a baseball bat, ready to tackle the intruder, only to find that the noise had been made by a mirror which for some reason had fallen off the chimney breast and yet remained un-cracked. James recalls: "I said, 'Stop messing Iggy!' and all of a sudden, there was an almighty crash in the kitchen. I was scared to go and see what had caused it, but finally opened the kitchen door to see that a unit had come off the wall, and was now lying in the middle of the floor as if it had been placed there. Stranger still, that unit had been above the fishtank, yet it had somehow fallen and not hit the tank – as if the thing had defied gravity."

The mystery of Iggy deepened a few months later when Mr Lamb was carrying out a loft conversion at his home. He found an old brass-framed photograph featuring the faded face of a young clean-cut man. When Mr Lamb brought it downstairs, his young son saw it and said, "That's Iggy!" The hairs on the back of his father's neck stood up when the child said those words.

The identity of the man in the picture is unknown. When I opened the back of the picture frame I found another photograph showing an unidentified elderly couple. So it looks like the mystery of just who Iggy really was will remain unresolved for the time being.

THE MYSTERY OF SPRING-HEELED JACK

In the whole of the *Haunted Liverpool, Haunted Cheshire* and *Haunted Wirral* series, there is one character alone who towers head and shoulders above the other supernatural entities and figures of folklore I have documented, and he is the legendary Spring-Heeled Jack, also known by an assortment of sinister aliases, such as Jumping Jack, the Leaping Terror, and the Jumping Man. The whole story about Spring-Heeled Jack's exploits – from his first appearance on Barnes Common in London in 1837 to his classic 'Last Bow' at Liverpool in 1904 – is covered in Volume One of *Haunted Liverpool*, but let us look at the Leaping Terror's Liverpool visits in a little more detail, and allow me to also present a new theory about Jack for your consideration.

During that grim season of 1888 which the Victorians called the Autumn of Terror, when Jack the Ripper, the most enigmatic killer in history, was carrying out his gruesome murders in London's East End, the city of Liverpool was visited by the other Jack, who generated as much fear and widespread panic as his shadowy namesake down in Whitechapel. This was Spring-Heeled Jack, of course, and one warm evening in August 1888, two off-duty police constables – John Cunningham and Tom Tinniswood of High Park Street, Toxteth, were standing on their doorsteps, chatting and smoking their pipes, when one of them caught a glimpse of a man crouched on the roof of the reservoir building just down the road, on the corner of Letitia Street. Tinniswood pointed to the suspicious-looking figure, which was silhouetted against the dusky sky, and Cunningham rushed into his home at Number 3 High Park Street and fetched his baton from the hallway.

Below their collar-less shirts, the two men still had on regulation police uniform trousers, held up by braces, and were wearing the sturdy, highly-polished thick-soled service boots, which were designed to endure hundreds of beat miles. In these boots they tip-toed down the street to the reservoir, and immediately attracted the attention of a loafer named Bob Lonsdale, who was sitting on his doorstep watching a lamplighter lighting the gas lamps on Twiss Street. A group of shawled women jangling on the corner of Digby Street stopped their gossiping and watched with intrigued faces as the two off-duty constables sneaked down to the reservoir.

"Oi! What are you doing up there?" Tinniswood called, with his head tilted back and his eyes trained on the pallid face of the rooftop prowler.

The man jumped, with his hands raised above his head as if he was surrendering. Cunningham swore in shock and stumbled backwards with his baton raised reflexively, expecting the suicidal maniac to land on him, but instead, the stranger seemed to somehow control his descent by opening his legs, and floating down. An assortment of gasps, profanities and screams echoed down High Park Street as people witnessed the bizarre descent. Within a heartbeat, the man's work-boots had hit the floor, and had 'bounced' him back up on to the roof of the reservoir. Hysterical laughter floated through the night air from above, and within the minute, the windows of the neighbourhood were being thrown and lifted open as the locals wondered who could be making such a disturbance. All the dogs of that quarter began to howl and bark at the sound of the unearthly shrieking laughter.

Old Mr Allen, a tallow chandler, stuck his night-capped head out of the window of his home and caught a dramatic glimpse of a man silhouetted against the full moon peeping over the chimney-pots of Admiral Street on the eastern horizon. This sinister figure sped at break-neck speed across the slanted slates of the roofs – then lifted up into the moonlit sky and sailed through the air in an arc which brought him back to earth on the cobbles of High Park Street. Police whistles pierced the air, and the superhuman visitor started to run at a phenomenal speed across the pavement towards Princes Road, where a PC Irving saw the figure pass him with the velocity of a steam train and vanish into the twilight. What the human mind can't make sense of, it struggles to explain away in desperation, and many of the people who didn't witness Spring-Heeled Jack's death-defying leaps that night said he had been nothing more than a sprightly burglar, or 'area-sneak' as they called such criminals in those times.

The High Park Street incident was by no means an isolated one. Chilling reports from further south in the city, from the prestigious suburbs of St Michael's-in-the-Hamlet and Aigburth, eventually reached the ears of the people of Toxteth. Two nights before the High Park Street appearance, a weird sprinting man was seen on Burdett Street, St Michael's-in-the-Hamlet. Just before midnight, a man named Peers was returning from a visit to his brother's home when he saw a top-hatted figure in the distance, walking down a deserted Burdett Street. A sea mist had drifted in from the Mersey and had settled on the streets of the area as a rolling ground vapour. Through the slight gas-lit haze, Peers could discern that the person was wearing an opera cloak.

All of a sudden, the cloaked man took off at an incredible speed. He bolted across Aigburth Road and jumped clean over the twelve-foot-tall garden wall of a mansion. Mr Peers slowed his gait and stared at the scene of this incredible feat first in astonishment then with dread; would the bizarre man come bounding back over that wall? Mr Peers wondered. The caped leaper never did, and the witness hurried home and reflected on what he had seen over a strong nightcap. Had it been a ghost or Old Nick himself in a top hat and cloak, playing a diabolical prank? Mr Peers slept with a burning candle and a Bible at his bedside that night, and on the following morning he was immensely interested to hear from his butler that there had been other sightings of the Leaping Terror in Aigburth, and also a report of the odd-looking ultra-athletic man at Otterspool Railway Station.

Weeks later, Spring-Heeled Jack turned up in the vicinity of Childwall, where, it is said, he was seen by none other than the illustrious millionaire Ralph Brocklebank, who was then the tenant of Childwall Hall. Dressed in black, and wearing a long cloak, Jack was seen running and leaping over moonlit fields one night by the quaintly named Cornelius Sherlock, an architect of some standing, but despite his status, people doubted his account of the leaping figure, and not one of the locals connected the incident with the reports of Spring-Heeled Jack which had been circulating in urban Liverpool.

Then, one evening, a comical yet creepy episode took place a couple of days after the Sherlock sighting. The organist of All Saint's Church, who, by a dark coincidence, had the surname 'Spring', was walking down a country lane in Childwall to the home of Sexton William Meadows, when he heard a cackle of laughter. It came from above – from the trees. James Spring gazed up into the branches and saw a hand reaching down to him. It seized his hair, and Spring ran off, yelping in terror, and toppled into a ditch, minus his wig. He got to his feet and saw the silhouette of a tall caped man standing in the lane. The organist ran off in abject terror, quoting the Lord's Prayer as the maniacal laughter of the cloaked fiend followed close on his heels.

Upon reaching Tower Yard, the residence of Sexton Meadows, James Spring started crying out for help, opened the gate and rushed to the door of the cottage. He hammered on the door, then went to the window and peered in at the Sexton, who did not recognise the organist at first because his 'hair' was missing. A policeman and a cow-keeper visited the tree where Spring-Heeled Jack had snatched the bald organist's wig, and found the toupée nestled among the leafy branches like a bird's nest.

The Reverend George Warr of All Saint's Church knew his organist was not a man to tell lies, and he believed a young irresponsible prankster was at large. The rural police station in Childwall was visited by a steady stream of local people who had also encountered the cloaked bogeyman, including a man who had watched the mysterious prowler gazing through the windows of Childwall Hall. Another witness actually claimed to have seen Spring-Heeled Jack scale the sandstone walls of the hall and run along its crenellated battlements.

The Leaping Terror was also reportedly seen gazing through the windows of the nearby Childwall Hotel, and he gave chase to two young drinkers from the pub who met him near the infamous 'Bloody Acre' – which is mentioned elsewhere in this book. In the weeks following these reports, Springy was seen at Huyton, Knotty Ash, Anfield and Everton, and in this latter district Jack's antics became outrageous.

Early one evening in September 1888, Spring-Heeled Jack was spotted on

Shaw Street, and the news of the sighting spread across the district and beyond within the hour. A number of pupils who had been playing in their classroom at St Francis Xavier's School rushed out to see the outlandish villain, but were greatly disappointed to learn that Jack had already been and gone, and now there were just groups of people standing about in the street, some describing the antics of the demonic rogue to worried-looking policemen.

The sightings of Spring-Heeled Jack then died down, but there were many jokers and lunatics who caused a number of scares across Liverpool in the aftermath of the Leaping Terror's visit. A butcher was fined after he painted a grinning face on a Chinese candle-lit lantern, attached it to a pole, and lifted it up to the window of an old woman with a weak heart on Richmond Row. Then, in October, a twenty-two-year-old man painted his face white, donned a long black coat, a wide felt hat, and ran screaming across Sheil Park, almost causing a nanny pushing a baby in a perambulator to faint. A week after that, on 19 October, 1888, a most curious report appeared in newspapers across England. The article stated that a woman of about sixty years of age had run screaming from Sheil Park after encountering a very sinister-looking man in black who had told her that he intended to, "kill as many women in Liverpool as in London", adding that he would send the ears of the first victim to the editor of the *Liverpool Daily Post.*

This man, who was probably a demented hoaxer taking advantage of the Jack the Ripper murders in the news, was never traced, but Scotland Yard sent detectives to Liverpool's Pier Head to keep watch on the steamers plying to and from America, just in case the Ripper was planning to flee to the States.

By mid-November, after the horrific killing of Mary Jeanette Kelly, Jack the Ripper was heard from no more, and around that time, Spring-Heeled Jack also ended his own reign of terror before vanishing into obscurity. The hysteria which Jack the Ripper caused with his baffling crimes eventually died down, but Spring-Heeled Jack's reputation as a bogeyman became firmly fixed in English ghost-lore, and the naughty children of the Victorian and Edwardian era were frightened into obedience by the mere mention of his name.

Sixteen years passed, and in September 1904, Spring-Heeled Jack returned to Liverpool, where he was said to have revisited a few of his old jumping grounds, including High Park Street. This time his eyes glowed, a strange phosphorescent gas was exhaled from his mouth, and his countenance was described as like that of the devil. The appearance of Spring-Heeled Jack at William Henry Street took place at the same time as an extraordinary haunting was being reported in the national press. The *Star* newspaper stated:

The exploits of a reputed ghost have kept several streets of Liverpool in an uproar this week. Lurid stories of the doings of the notorious Spring-Heeled Jack, who some years ago frightened half the women and children of the city, were recalled by present scenes. Pieces of brick, old bottles and other missiles came hurtling down the chimneys of the haunted house. Where they came from baffled the vigilance of watchers. The annoyance was so persistent and the terror among the neighbours so great that the residents of the house left hurriedly and the place was closed.

There was great confusion in the national and local press between the reports of Spring-Heeled Jack and a violent poltergeist that was causing havoc in Everton. That week, there were dark rumours circulating in Everton of something being conjured up at a séance at a house that was situated on William Henry Street and even one reference to demonic possession. George and Priscilla Pierpoint of Everton Road, were visiting relatives on that September night when Spring-Heeled Jack visited the neighbourhood, and the entire family of five saw the remarkable drama take place at about half-past seven. Henry Pierpoint, aged ten, sister Edith, aged nine, and younger brother George, aged seven, watched open-mouthed as a man came floating across Whitley Gardens at treetop level, screaming with laughter with a crowd of locals, headed by a policeman, on his trail. He escaped his pursuers by passing over the park railings before landing with a gentle thud on the pavement of Westbourne Street. He then ran off at an amazing speed into the dark warren of streets, and was later seen climbing the steeple of St Francis Xavier's Church. On the following evening, on William Henry Street, a man climbed out of his garret window and on to the roof, screaming, "My wife is the Devil! He has possessed her!"

The police turned up and tried to talk the man down, but he began to foam at the mouth, and in some reports he talked in tongues and recited Biblical scripture before walking across the slates and leaping on to neighbouring roofs in a suicidal manner, until the police used a fireman's ladder to seize the 'maniac'. This man seemed to have superhuman strength and it took four policemen to subdue him and make an arrest. A burly policeman, Constable 243B, had his arm broken by the man, who exhibited all the signs of possession.

In the Bible there are numerous accounts of how a person possessed by evil spirits can become endowed with superhuman strength and may even break the chains that fetter him. Another less-known aspect of possession is the levitation of the victim. In 1906, a South African girl named Clara Germana Cele, levitated whilst she was possessed, and fell to the ground as Holy Water was sprinkled upon her. Simon Magus, also known as Simon the Sorcerer, a Samaritan occultist who is mentioned in the Bible's Book of Acts, was also said to have levitated during his possession by a spirit. The list goes on, and this brings us to an intriguing possibility. Were the sightings of Spring-heeled Jack - which span sixty-seven years from his debut on Barnes Common in 1837 to his Grand Finale in 1904 – actually a succession of several individuals who were actually taken over, or possessed, by some demonic entity? My senior researcher Kevin Roach, of Liverpool's Central Library, unearthed the following intriguing article, from the *Liverpool Echo*, dated 13 August 1904:

A HUMAN KANGAROO

Something like a panic was caused in the streets of Lisbon last week by the extraordinary antics of a young man named Albano, who suffers from a most exceptional form of epilepsy, during which he runs rapidly on all fours like an animal, cries, grunts and barks, and displays almost supernatural agility.

Suddenly seized with a fit in the street, Albano leaped over the heads of the terrified passers-by, rushed into electric cars by the door, and jumped out of the window. A flight of fifteen wide stone steps was cleared at a flying leap. Finally he stumbled and appeared to come to his senses. The unfortunate man is to be sent to a lunatic asylum.

Could Albano have been possessed by something demonic which caused him to fly through the air? Epilepsy is conveniently blamed, but how would such a mental illness enable a man to leap over the heads of people and clear fifteen stone steps in a single bound? A month after that bizarre incident in Lisbon, Spring-Heeled Jack arrived at the port of Liverpool. I wonder if any ships from Portugal came to the Liverpool Docks in September 1904, carrying someone who had become possessed with the same demon that turned Albano into a hyper-athletic madman?

If demonic possession is responsible for the reports of the glowing-eyed, manic, Spring-Heeled Jack, could the demon still possess a person today? In

1985, the Liverpool Star *newspaper interviewed Edward Christopherson, a pensioner who said he had seen Spring-Heeled Jack in the 1920s. Edward was sitting on a wall outside his family's home on the corner of Warwick Street and Wolfe Street, when he saw something very peculiar indeed. Edward recalled: "I was just sitting there minding my own business when this bloke walks past on the other side of Warwick Street. He was just an ordinary bloke, dressed in workingmen's clothes. I didn't think anything of it until he turned into Wolfe Street. Suddenly, he stopped, looked up at the building beside him and then jumped up on to the roof!"*

Edward immediately ran into his house and told his family what he had just seen. His father, who was sitting reading a newspaper by the fire, said, rather nonchalantly: "That'll be Spring-Heeled Jack."

"I was completely nonplussed at what I had just seen," Edward reminisced, "but it appears that Jack was well-known in Toxteth at that time and nobody batted an eyelid when I told them what I had seen. When you see these athletes doing the high jump with those poles, what do they do – about 15 feet? This bloke jumped at least 30 feet without anything."

OTHER TITLES BY TOM SLEMEN